ODYSSEUS
FOUND

ODYSSEUS FOUND

*A Royal Tomb, a Hero Cult, and
the Birth of a Legend*

Konstantin N. Kokkolis

Self Published

Konstantin N. Kokkolis

Odysseus Found: A Royal Tomb, a Hero Cult, and the Birth of a Legend

Cover Photo: K. N. Kokkolis, View of Argostoli Bay from Kangelisses, Kokolata. Kefalonia, Greece.

Dedicated to

My parents, Nikolaos and Amalia

"In fact, the entire plot of Odysseus' travels is interlaced with diction that otherwise connotes the theme of sunset followed by sunrise. To put it more bluntly, the epic plot of Odysseus' travels operates on an extended solar metaphor, as Frame argues in adducing the internal evidence of Homeric theme and diction."

- GREGORY NAGY, (1973, p. 139)

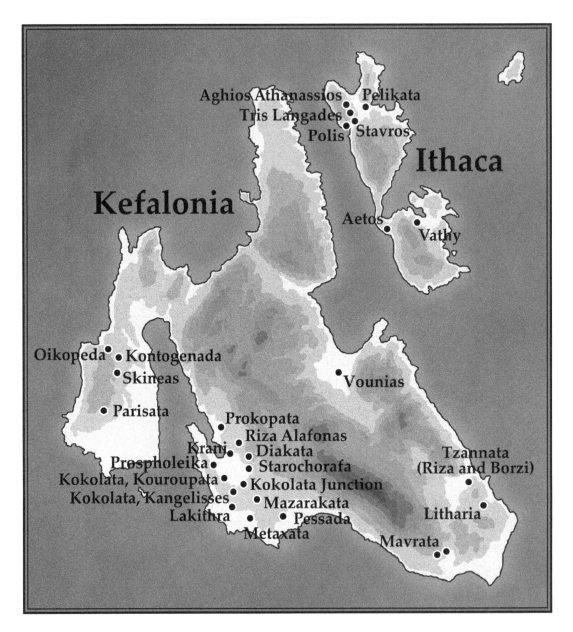

Central Ionian Sea, Late Bronze Age (1550-1050 BC) settlements (as evidenced by architectural remains or high-density pottery sherds) and cemeteries. Not all sites were contemporary to each other. One location seemed to have been significant in terms of population, and thus we can conclude it was the most influential of the central Ionian.

CONTENTS

ILLUSTRATIONS

FIGURES

Tables

PREFACE

A NEW CANDIDATE FOR HOMERIC ITHACA

In the summer of 2020, while inspecting a family property, I noticed many ancient remains of various eras. I knew archaeologists had previously explored an area not far from there, which piqued my interest. Coincidentally, an acquaintance happened to be nearby while his goats grazed. I told him the area seemed full of ancient remains. He took me to a heavily wooded area of the property and showed me what appeared to be a peculiar ancient installation. A grand stone entrance with cyclopean boulder remnants leads to this installation (and two other large stone entrances in the area leading to a flat hilltop.)

I later realized it was an open-air cult center in the village of Kokolata in a place called Archangelo, named after a long abandoned church nearby. It was a very unusual multi-level installation comprising a throne and many large carved boulders, two of which were symmetrical, pointing to each other. After many months of observation and brush clearing, a realization dawned on me one early evening in late May 2021. As the sun was setting, I was standing near what I later understood to be the podium or observation point, and I noticed the setting sun was almost aligned with one of the carved linear edges of a boulder. Knowing that the summer solstice was only a month away, I planned to bring photography equipment on my visit at the summer solstice – both morning and evening. Sure enough, on that day, the sun was aligned with the "summer boulder" at sunrise and sunset.

In a past field survey, Bronze Age potsherds, many Middle Helladic, were found at a nearby site. Christina Souyoudzoglou-Haywood, former Director of the Irish Institute of Hellenic Studies at Athens and current Adjunct faculty at the UCD School of Classics, named the site Kokolata-Junction. She concluded there must have been a sizable Middle

Bronze Age settlement nearby. Archangelo is about 250 meters from Kokolata-Junction. Archangelo, I believe, is that settlement.

Having realized that a solar deity was worshipped at Archangelo, I looked to this region's existing Bronze Age sites with the sun and solstices in mind. I did not just look at the ground but using GPS and merging computer simulations of topography with the sky; I looked at the horizon and ancient sky from these sacred sites for clues.

Like countless others who have found ancient remains in the central Ionian Sea, I began thinking of any connection to *The Odyssey*. I believed the answers would lie not in geographically "decoding" *The Odyssey* for "Homeric Ithaca" but in searching for the actual civilization that would have created the initial myth of Odysseus. I needed to know who they were, what they worshipped, and how they worshipped. That, to me, would explain how their local hero, centuries later, would become the protagonist of an epic.

As my research and exploration of the Kokolata countryside progressed, I pivoted to other disciplines. From countless online searches with terms such as "*Odyssey*," "solar," and "Bronze Age Greece," I began looking to Minoan glyptic art and its various interpretations by prominent scholars for more clues. In Minoan seal rings, we frequently see images of a divine couple associated with the sun and moon. Moreover, my research led me to astronomic interpretations of *The Odyssey*: the allegories of solar and lunar cycles. I also began exploring comparative mythology and how *The Odyssey* could be deconstructed into multiple motifs/components going back much deeper in history, well before what many believe was the period of the fall of Troy.

That is when an old local leader's story began to unfold.

I believe that the Bronze Age inhabitants of the Argostoli-Kokolata-Livatho area, with their administrative center in Archangelo, Kokolata, had a leader and were an independent region in Southwest Kefalonia, possibly ruling over most if not all of the island at one time. I believe this leader had cleverly devised a way to gain immortality - to be worshipped along with the sun. I finally understood his thought process: I knew where the tomb would be.

The later (end of Submycenaean/Early Archaic period) establishment of an acropolis at the nearby Krani hilltop with its new foundation myths and places of worship caused the demise of the old Bronze Age Archangelo center and nearby hero worship hilltop. With the end of its influence and local hero worship ritual, the fading of local memories ensued. His story, however, took on a life of its own. His story had already conquered Greece.

K.N. Kokkolis
Kokolata, Kefalonia

SOFTWARE PROGRAMS USED IN MY SEARCH

Sky simulations in this book are all from the open-source planetarium program Stellarium. (http://stellarium.org) I also used Google Earth, with specific GPS locations, to create terrain simulations which I imported into Stellarium. This way, horizons covered the correct sky areas in Stellarium. Thus I could predict where a sunrise or sunset would have taken place relative to the horizon and when. I could also visualize which constellations passed over certain areas of the horizon. Against real-world sunrise and sunset tests, I found the simulation to be very accurate and the time to be off by only 2-4 minutes for completion of sunset or sunrise at specific locations on the horizon, which could be explained by weather and atmospheric conditions.

Furthermore, I have also used just Google Earth to confirm the sunrise and sunset locations on the horizon. However, Google Earth shows the current year's solstices, so the sun's location is off by about a sun width due to the change in the earth's tilt since ancient times. Nonetheless, using Google Earth was useful in initial examinations of sunrises and sunsets, as seen from Bronze Age sacred sites. In the sky simulation photos that follow, I superimposed pictures of the actual horizon onto the Stellarium screenshot to have better accuracy between foreground objects such as graves and locations on the horizon where a particular solstice sunset or sunrise would occur.

A NOTE ON SPELLINGS AND LOCATION NAMES

One frustrating aspect of researching this topic is that in any literature about Kefalonia, the spellings of many locations vary a lot. For example, Kefalonia has also been spelled: Cephalonia, Cefalonia, Kephallonia, Kefallenia – the older Greek being the last, which resembles most the "Kephallenes" of *The Odyssey* and *Iliad*. The village of Kokolata and the namesake of the Venetian-era migrant inhabitants can also be spelled as Kokkolata, with a double "K." The greater region this book focuses on has been referred to as Argostoli-Livatho. I may frequently refer to it as Kokolata-Livatho because I believe the area around the village of Kokolata was at least a Bronze Age sacred center and very likely, by association, the administrative center of the region, if not the entire island. The area of Archangelo in Kokolata is named after an abandoned post-Byzantine church near the solar cult center.

ABBREVIATIONS USED IN TEXTS

Early Helladic	EH	Early Bronze Age	EBA
Middle Helladic	MH	Middle Bronze Age	MBA
Late Helladic	LH	Late Bronze Age	LBA

Bronze Age chronologies by regions/countries vary. When we refer to Greek (excluding Crete) periods of the Bronze Age, the term "Helladic" is used. For example, the Middle Bronze Age in Greece is called the Middle Helladic period. The word Protogeometric is the period after the Mycenaean era. It was named such because of the style of pottery used during that period. Submycenaean or (Early) Iron Age is also used for that period. The following two pages show a timeline of the Greek Bronze Age sub-periods.

A CHRONOLOGY OF THE GREEK BRONZE AGE WITH AN EMPHASIS ON KEFALONIA

The following quoted excerpts on the timeline are from Christina Souyoudzoglou-Haywood, *The Ionian Islands in the Bronze and Early Iron Age 3000-800 BC*, Liverpool 1999.

B.C.	Period	
3000	EARLY HELLADIC I	Greek speaking Indo Europeans were probably already just north of Greece at this point, part of the gradual southern migration into the Greek mainland and islands which begins around 1900 B.C.
2500	EARLY HELLADIC II	The Minoan civilization, the first civilization in Greece, develops during this period, and judging by the cult center at Archangelo Kokolata in Kefalonia, the Minoan influence would have reached Kefalonia by at least the EH III or MH I.
2200	EARLY HELLADIC III	"Of the listed sites only the newly discovered Kokkolata Junction may yield more information if explored further. Its location in the Argostoli plain indicates that the advantages of the district and of the bay of Argostoli had began to be recognised. The preliminary survey showed it to be a fairly large settlement that may prove to have already been a permanently occupied village in the EBA." (Souyoudzoglou-Haywood, p. 46)
2000		
1550	MIDDLE HELLADIC	"The vicinity of Kangelisses to the site of Kokkolata Junction, which lies just 700m to the south, as well as some pottery types which they have in common, suggest that there is a possible connection between the cemetery and the settlement. The question deserves to be investigated further. The tombs, especially if they were part of a tumulus, and their wealth of pottery would seem to indicate that Kangelisses was the burial ground of a privileged social group." (Souyoudzoglou-Haywood, p.47)
1500	LATE HELLADIC I	

1500 B.C.	LATE HELLADIC II	Little evidence of change in the Kokolata Livatho area of Kefalonia, possibly due to a consistent use of pottery style from the Middle Helladic period.
1400 / 1300	LATE HELLADIC IIIA	Mycenaeanization of Kefalonia "There are strong indications that the 14th century, when tholos tombs and chamber tombs make their earliest appearance, was the time of major expansion into Kefalonia, and that LH IIIA2–B/C was the period of major consolidation, particularly in the regions of Argostoli Livatho (Prokopata, Mazarakata, Metaxata, Lakkithra)..." (Souyoudzoglou-Haywood, p.136)
	EARLY HELLADIC III	
1200	COLLAPSE OF MYCENAEAN WORLD	"...the cemeteries suggest continuity of habitation in all the districts. At Argostoli-Livatho none of the cemeteries established in LH IIIA2–B were abandoned and there are new tombs added to the cemeteries of Mazarakata, Metaxata and Lakkithra in LH III B/C and in LH IIIC. Diakata, with its adjacent habitation site of Starochorafa, is a newly-founded LH IIIC site..." (Souyoudzoglou-Haywood, p.138)
1100	LATE HELLADIC IIIC	
1050	PROTOGEOMETRIC/ EARLY IRON AGE/ SUBMYCENEAN	"The abandonment of the Kefalonian cemeteries, particularly those of Argostoli -Livatho, took place sometime between 1075 and 1050/40 BC." (ibid p.139)

1

INTRODUCTION

A BRIEF HISTORY OF THE SEARCH FOR ITHACA

The search for "Ithaca," as described by Homer, has been an ongoing endeavor since ancient times. Despite the many theories and explorations of the last 2300 years and beyond – from Eratosthenes and Strabo to Schliemann, and most recently Bittlestone in Paliki, Metaxas/Randsborg in Poros/Tzannata and T. Papadopoulos at Agios Athanasios in Ithaca, results have been inconclusive. Homer's accounts and descriptions in *The Odyssey*, written centuries after the end of the Bronze Age, cannot be taken as a historical series of events or a geography lesson. Analyzing *The Odyssey* using comparative mythology, astronomical allegories, and the current archaeological evidence shows us a much more complex multi-layered literary work. The more critical question is, if there was an individual behind the pre-Homeric Odyssey myth, what type of society did he live in, and how did he become so famous living on the edge of the Greek world? The bizarre stories about him can not be taken seriously as clues. Classical scholars using comparative mythology have shown that many parts of *The Odyssey* have roots in the deeper past, often shared by other cultures. Similarly, astronomers have identified allegories that have nothing to do with the story. How did this come about?

Of all the areas explored through excavations between the two islands, only one region appears to have had a significant population throughout the Bronze Age, given the number of tombs and evidence of settlements. It is the area of Argostoli-Kokolata-Livatho in the SW region of the island of Kefalonia. Livatho is the hilly region beyond the Krania valley in southwestern Kefalonia and continues to the base of Mt. Ainos in Lourdas. In Venetian times, the village of Kokolata was called Kokolata Livatho (Ital. sp. Cocolata Livato) to distinguish it from the other Kokolata village in the north of the island, called Cocolata Erisso, Erisso being the region of the northern peninsula of Kefalonia.

At Tzannata/Borzi, in southeast Kefalonia, a large tholos tomb, indicative of a wealthy local family, was identified by resident Gerasimos Metaxas. At the top of the hill near the tomb, archaeologist and then Director Emeritus of Antiquities Antonis Vasilakis uncovered a small Late Helladic ellipsoid structure built above an old destroyed, Late Helladic building. Below that were remains of a late Middle Helladic or early Late Helladic structure. (Vasilakis, 2020) However, nothing else indicative of a nearby center was found. The fact that this grand tholos tomb was located below the building(s) without commanding views and with nothing else in the immediate area, such as a cult center, or grand entrance, tells me that this area was not a significant center. I also believe the builders of this tholos tomb wanted to show a solar connection to the older MH cemetery at Kangelisses – in my view, the most important and influential Bronze Age cemetery on the island. (A video showing the spatial relationship between the cemetery at Kangelisses, Kokolata, and the Tzannata tholos is available at www.odysseusfound.blog). Overall, the Tzannata/Borzi area seems to me to have been a low-populated area that functioned as a very successful commercial node on the Ionian sea route. Access to the Kefalonian fir of nearby Mount Ainos would likely have also provided a material that was harvested and traded.

In Ithaca, there was only one site of prominence: Aghios Athanasios. It has also been called the School of Homer since the early 1800s. That second name, predictably, has drawn countless tourists. The site, recently re-excavated by archaeologist Thanasis Papadopoulos, seems like a promising site. (Papadopoulos, 2022) Although what we see today is a predominately Hellenistic period structure, the area did contain scatterings of Bronze Age sherds, a well house, some Bronze Age foundation walls, a metal shop, and a possible altar. There is also evidence of a Mycenaean era structure, and to quote Papadopoulos:

However, the case for Aghios Athanasios has been invalidated at the time of this writing. On September 18th, 2022, a presentation was given by Grigoris Grigorakakis, the Director of the Ephorate of Antiquities for Kefalonia and Ithaca, and Yannos G. Lolos, professor of prehistoric archaeology, University of Ioannina. The new conclusion is that the site was a Bronze Age cult center with no evidence of a palace.

Furthermore, we have no evidence regarding the island's name during the Bronze Age. In the conclusion of this book, I analyze the issues that have arisen with locating Homeric Ithaca and if it were ever an actual place name during the Bronze Age.

PREHISTORIC MIGRATIONS TO GREECE

The early ancient Greek civilization was an assimilation of two culturally unique migrations. One began in the Neolithic era and continued westwards and northwards, reaching most of Europe, and the other in the Bronze Age, which comprised a Greek-speaking population that later assimilated with natives in mainland Greece and became known as the Mycenaean civilization.

NEOLITHIC FARMER MIGRATION

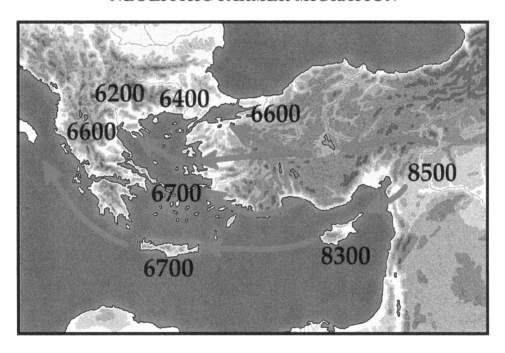

Fig. 1. Dates of migration. Source material: Gronenborn/Horejs/Börner/Ober 2021.2 (RGZM/ÖAI).

The map (Fig. 1) shows the Neolithic farmer migration from Anatolia/Near East to Greece. It continued west and north, reaching most of Europe. A part of this migration remained in Crete and became the Minoan civilization before the arrival of Greek Speakers in Greece. Judging from Minoan glyptic art, a solar goddess was likely the prime deity.

INDO-EUROPEAN (PROTO-GREEK SPEAKERS) MIGRATION

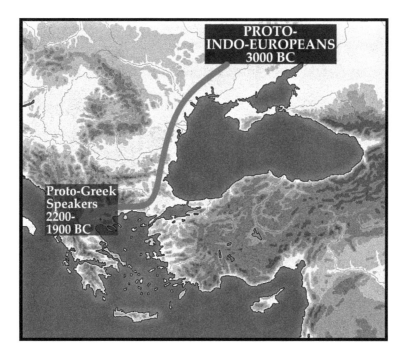

Fig. 2. Migration dates are estimations derived from DNA and linguistic analyses from multiple sources.

This map (Fig. 2) shows the Indo-European migration of Proto-Greek Speakers to the central Balkans and, ultimately, southward to Greece. The Eurasian steppe north of the Black Sea has been suggested as the area from which the Proto-Greek speakers may have initially migrated. The Greek Speakers settling within the Greek mainland would have occurred 1900-1600BC. By the Late Helladic, the assimilation would have been complete, and judging from recent DNA analyses, one can conclude that steppe migration or Neolithic ancestry was irrelevant in determining social status. (Lazaridis I., et al. 2022)

2

THE SOLAR CULT CENTER
AT ARCHANGELO, KOKOLATA

ADMINISTRATIVE REGIONS IN SW KEFALONIA:
PAST AND PRESENT

We begin with my first discovery, the solar cult center. Although archaeologists have not yet fully explored the installation, it is reasonable to conclude it is a Bronze Age solar cult center. Further in this chapter, I compare this installation with Minoan glyptic art, how it marked the solstice sunsets and sunrises, and how I dated it using the star Arcturus. Moreover, its location and the fact that it contains a throne give the impression the area may have been not only a religious center but also an administrative center. Looking at past administrative centers in the greater region provides some context.

Historically, the southwest region of Kefalonia has always had an administrative center or capital. Since late Venetian times to English rule until today, the island's capital has been Argostoli. Before that, during most of Venetian rule and the late Byzantine period, the island's administrative center was at the hilltop where the Venetian castle of Saint George sits. The island split into four independent centers during the Archaic to the Roman period – known as the tetrapolis. The Krani acropolis was one of those centers. Before the Archaic period, we have little information about the island's administrative region(s).

About a hundred years ago, archaeologists Panagis Kavvadias, Sylvia Benton, Nikolaos Kyparisses, and Spiros Marinatos excavated the acropolis at Krani in search of a Bronze Age center. Bronze age ceramics were found, but nothing evident of a Bronze Age acropolis.

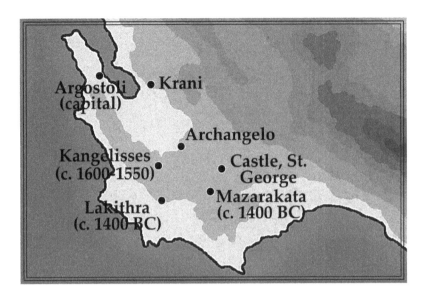

Fig. 3. Present and past administrative centers and major
Bronze Age cemeteries (with dates), SW Kefalonia

Looking at the mortuary landscape, we see that the only Middle Bronze Age cemetery in all of Kefalonia is the cemetery at Kangelisses, Kokolata. Furthermore, two of the largest cemeteries on the island at Mazarakata and Lakithra, constructed about two hundred years after Kangelisses during the Late Helladic, are SE and SW of Archangelo. Their locations suggest a type of "sprawl" had occurred similar to what we see in many old cities today, with the oldest cemeteries in their centers. Due to this fact, I believe that a Bronze Age center or main settlement could not have been located at the acropolis at Krani at that time. It wouldn't have been logical for the newer cemeteries, which served many families, to have been so far away. Funerary processions to the cemeteries from Krani would have been long and tedious. Whereas from Kokolata, a funerary procession to either the Lakithra cemetery or the larger Mazarakata cemetery would have only required less than an hour of walking. Therefore, it would be more logical that the Bronze Age center would be closer to Kangelisses, somewhere in Kokolata.

DISCOVERING THE SOLAR CULT CENTER

During the pandemic period of 2020-2021, while exploring the Kokolata countryside with Christina Souyoudzoglou-Haywood's field survey results in mind, I found what seemed to be an unusual megalithic installation beneath a thick cover of trees. My first thoughts were Celtic or Druidic, not Greek; although admittedly illogical even then, it was because I felt that the people who likely gathered and worshipped there had a deep connection to the geological phenomenon of cascading boulders on the terraced hillside. I felt that the trees that grew in the area back then, as they do today, were worshipped as well. It didn't look "Greek" to me, at least not the image of ancient Greece that most people have. The megalithic installation was not intrusive to the natural environment but was part of it. Even what I eventually realized was a stone throne was minimally carved. My initial impression was of an open-air nature sanctuary. After much research, I began to understand the pre-Mycenaean history of Greece - the era of Neolithic farmers that likely had migrated from Anatolia, part of the same migration that also culminated in the culturally influential Minoan civilization on Crete. It was also the same migration that spread through Europe, the farmers that created megalithic solar installations such as Stonehenge in England and many others in France and Germany.

I eventually discovered this installation's solar/calendrical use. From then on, I began interpreting the natural landscape surrounding the previously explored Bronze Age sites with solstice and equinox sunsets and sunrises in mind. In addition, ancient remains surrounding the solar cult center give me the impression that a large, significant settlement existed there. I discuss this in more detail in the chapter on the spatial relations of Bronze Age sites.

At this point, I want to emphasize that a video I produced better shows the layout of the solar cult center than any written description. There is a link to the video on my blog at www.odysseusfound.blog.

Fig. 4. Solar cult center symmetrical boulders

I took this photo while standing on the "observation" pedestal – a circular stone formation still protruding from the soil. The two boulders ahead were symmetrically carved to form two arrows that face each other. The top lines seem to point to the solstice sunsets. A central arrow-shaped boulder above marks the equinox sunset. The boulder only appears to have been carved at its top third to form a triangle pointing skywards.

Fig. 5. Solar cult center "equinox" stone. The sun's intensity is low due to the tree
on the property above blocking much of the sun.

Figures 5a and 5b on the following two pages show the two symmetrical boulders viewed
from above. They are arrow-shaped and point to an elevated horizon where the sun rises
on solstices. Above in figure 5 is the equinox stone, with the equinox sunset "resting" on
the triangle's apex. I took the photo above in figure 5 while standing on the dirt ledge
above the two boulders. All boulders seem to have eroded to a degree. The summer
boulder (fig. 5b) may appear less "arrow-like" because an additional arrow bulges on its
top surface, which I will describe next.

Fig. 5a. Winter boulder at winter solstice sunrise. Bronze Age sunrise would have been a little more to the right.

Fig. 5b. Summer boulder at summer solstice sunrise. The sun would have been a little more to the left during the Bronze Age.

DATING THE CULT CENTER AT ARCHANGELO: THE STAR ARCTURUS, 1850 BC, SHOWS THE WAY

Fig. 6. Carved arrow on the top of the summer boulder pointing towards the horizon above.

At the top of the summer solstice boulder, there is a carved triangle/arrow pointing northeast. This feature of the boulder seemed purposeful and took almost a year for me to understand. At first, I thought it could be the northern lunar standstill moon rise that it pointed to, which is the most northeasterly point on the horizon the moon rises – a long cycle explained in another chapter. However, after creating a simulation on the Stellarium planetary program with the local topography superimposed, I realized that the point on the horizon above the arrow is an area of the Troiannata Mountains located between the polar circle and the northern lunar standstill moonrise.

I learned of the Minoan peak sanctuaries when researching Bronze Age installations that served as calendars/solar observatories. The only significant celestial body that would have regularly risen at the horizon in this area would have been the star Arcturus, the brightest star of the constellation Boötes. Arcturus is a star that Minoans marked at some Minoan peak sanctuaries along with the sun and moon. (Blomberg and Henriksson, 1997) It is also the brightest star in the northern celestial hemisphere, which gives it additional significance.

Today, the star Arcturus rises much further to the east than the north due to the earth's tilt/axis change since ancient times. I used Stellarium planetary software to see when the star Arcturus had risen at this point on the horizon in the past. Well before November, Arcturus would have been visible above the Argostoli area. Then it would have disappeared below the horizon and the mountains and reappeared about seven hours later above the Troiannata Mountains at the same location.

I went back to Stellarium and experimented with different centuries BC to see when the star Arcturus rose where the arrow points to the horizon. I found the date of the heliacal rising of Arcturus (approx. September 9), which is when it rises from the horizon just before sunrise.

Fig. 7. Heliacal rising Arcturus, Stellarium sky/Landscape photo and label by author.
The location where the arrow on the summer boulder points.

The best date that matches when Arcturus would have risen at that location on the horizon would have been approximately 1850 BC. (The arrow is very worn, and many branches above affect the field of view.) I would add or subtract 50 years for the best estimate in case of errors, but I am inclined to believe it is closer to 1900 BC.

By 1650 BC, however, the ancients may have noticed that the star Arcturus had shifted quite enough to the right. Though they wouldn't have known the scientific reason, the shift is due to the gradual changing tilt of the earth's axis. By 1600 BC, they would have been sure of it. The difference would have been pronounced by then.

In the next chapter, I conclude that the cemetery at Kangelisses was a hybrid type of cemetery - part Kurgan-influenced, part Aegean Solar-based religion. Since its construction would have been around 1600 BC – 1550 BC, maybe the star Arcturus was also marked at the Kangelisses cemetery.

Let's see Kangelisses and where the star Arcturus would have risen around 1600 BC.

Fig. 8. Stellarium simulation of the heliacal rising of the star Arcturus
Photo of a cist grave at the Kangelisses cemetery, 1600 BC.

Fig. 8 shows the northern view from the observation point at the Kangelisses cemetery. The heliacal rising of the star Arcturus is above the center of cist grave #4. As we will see in the next chapter, the cist graves served as markers, and there was one central cist grave that functioned as the observation point, similar to the pedestal at Archangelo when viewing the solstice and equinox sunsets.

The existing body of research on the Kangelisses ceramics found in the cist graves had already dated the cemetery to the late Middle Helladic period. Therefore my research based on astronomy is consistent with archaeological dating of the earliest material culture, the contents of the cist graves at Kangelisses.

Did the ancients realize the stars "wander" due to the change in the tilt of the earth's axis? That is very unlikely. But they must have known that, unlike the sun and moon, which have changed little since then, the stars noticeably shifted from past locations.

Fig. 9. Throne at the Archangelo cult center

If my dating of the Archangelo cult center (c. 1850 BC) is correctly based on the rising star Arcturus, then the throne at Archangelo is much older than the throne room at Knossos.

MINOAN GLYPTIC ART TELLS A STORY

If the cult center's construction is circa 1850 BC, it would most likely have predated the arrival of the early Greek-speaking Indo-Europeans in Kefalonia. Hence, the locals would have followed a Minoan-type religion. An analysis of Minoan iconography on seal rings can help us better understand this cult center. Seal rings (also called signet rings) were rings with an oval face, intricately carved to show a religious scene. The rings served as stamps; in that way, one could stamp their ring in wet clay or soft wax to leave an impression and show ownership of an object or authority on a document.

British archaeologist Sir Arthur Evans claimed that in the open-air worship centers in Crete, the Minoans believed that the gods and goddesses temporarily inhabited the trees and stones (Evans, 1901). His conclusion was based on his observations of Minoan glyptic art found on seal rings in Mycenae and Crete. Therefore people built and visited these sanctuaries to be close to the deities. It is important to note that these sanctuaries were open-air sanctuaries. Boulders and trees were common features that connected people with nature and the gods.

The throne at Archangelo and the surrounding stones were merely cut or carved to serve their individual uses - and no more. Aesthetics was set aside. It was as if the builders respected the natural form of the rocks to a great extent. The seat of the throne is large and wide, and if we look at some Minoan seal rings, we have a better picture of who the throne may have been symbolically intended.

In Minoan iconography, we often see a large female seated, never the male. The fact that she is sitting gives the impression of importance – either of royalty or a primary deity.

Fig. 10. Gold signet ring: Divine Couple, HM number 1710, Poros, Crete

The solar goddess on Minoan seal rings is always depicted as a large woman, similar to many Stone Age Venus figurines interpreted by many as fertility goddesses. One view of the throne at Knossos, from its first days of discovery: judging by the shape of the seat, it was the throne of a female, a high priestess, not King Minos. Was the throne at Archangelo used by a female representative of the solar goddess? Was it used as a representation of the solar goddess, but no one sat on it? I have sat on the throne, which is constructed for human proportions, and the front area beneath the seat is recessed so one can bend their knees and place their feet somewhat beneath the seat.

If we look to the palace of Knossos for clues, I think we can reasonably speculate how worshippers used this cult center and what the throne symbolized. I believe it represented authority and an area near it was an administrative center. Ute Günkel-Maschek analyzes the enthroned woman we see at Knossos in Minoan art as follows:

> "In imagery the palace itself is represented not only as a focus of ritual gesture, but first and foremost as the earthly abode of the divinity and the seat of its human agent. Therefore, the establishing of the enthroned authority at Knossos and the elite's ostentatious interaction with her appear to have been two manifestations of the same strategy: to consolidate the dominant position of specifically this palatial centre and its ruling class." (2016)

RITUAL WORSHIP AND SYMBOLISM AT THE CULT CENTER

There are numerous concave and angular carvings in the boulders around the cult center, including one large recess at the back of the throne. These concave carvings are extremely common at this cult center – even on boulders further off that do not currently seem to serve a purpose. I assume that if the locals believed the deities temporarily "inhabited" the stones during ceremonies, these might have been carved to serve as symbolic "entry points" for the gods.

The following two Minoan seal/signet rings show how worshippers would have used this cult center.

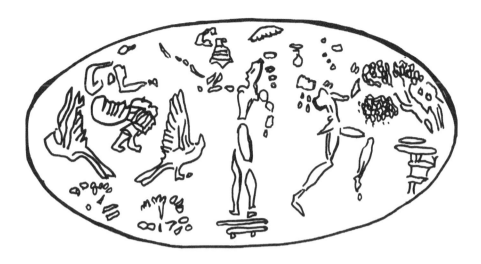

Fig. 11. "Sacred Conversation" seal ring (Ikarou St., Poros, Crete)

A man (worshipper) shakes/pulls a tree (fig. 11), and another man embraces a boulder (fig. 12). Many scholars have interpreted that the two male worshippers are engaging in activities that bring to them a deity – an epiphany.

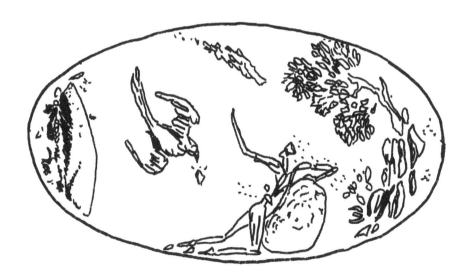

Fig. 12. Sellopoulo tomb 4 seal ring, Knossos

Baetyl worship was the worship of stones believed to have religious value. The cult center at Archangelo has such boulders and very likely was full of trees as it is today. In the Sellopoulo signet ring image (Fig. 12), we see a man embracing a boulder. At the same time, a bird appears – possibly representing an epiphany of a deity in the form of a bird.

Fig. 13. Photo of the dromos at the cult center. Three baetyls are numbered on the left. The throne is just beyond the third baetyl.

A narrowing dromos/path leads to the throne at the worship center. The dromos/path is bordered on the left by three large flat-faced (mostly unworked) boulders, and the hillside opposite has three carved recesses created by a series of pointed boulders. After analyzing the signet rings, one can conclude that the religious motifs and environment on the signet rings match this open-air cult center very well. Are the three boulders on the left representative of the three seasons people of the Bronze Age followed? An analysis of the Bronze Age calendar is in the conclusion of this book.

One can imagine worshippers at the Archangelo cult center pulling the trees and embracing the boulders to beckon the deities to visit them. Quite possibly, the throne was constructed for the female deity to "visit" them as they engaged in the rituals involving natural elements of the environment, such as the trees and stones. Furthermore, the solar deity's earthly representative could have used the throne while her partner, staff in hand, was on the pedestal above, observing a solstice or equinox.

Staffs are also frequently depicted on seal rings. One possible explanation for their use would be aligning a sunrise or sunset with a foreground object such as a pointed boulder or grave. At two locations at the cult center, where the viewer stands to witness a solstice, there are holes in the exposed bedrock below. They seem to have been placements for a staff to align a foreground object (boulder) with the sun.

I have experimented with using a simple shaft of a garden tool as a makeshift staff. Suppose one aligns it with a sunrise or sunset on a distant mountain horizon with a foreground object nearby and looks with one eye open. In that case, it helps one focus on the alignment between the sun and object while minimizing any damage to the eye. The sun's halo is visible without causing eye strain (and I would hope no permanent retinal damage). However, this does not work mid-day, when the sun's rays are much more substantial. At sunrise or sunset, though, as the sun's rays are not as strong, it actually works.

The cult center also has an upper-level staging or ceremonial area that includes the pedestal/observation point, the two large "solstice" boulders, and the "equinox stone." I noticed that if one were to stand at the pedestal, they could also address an audience below, as the cult center area is terraced with at least four levels. Thus the highest level is the rock ledge that functions as the horizon for the sunsets and where the equinox stone protrudes. The second level is where the tops of the boulders are located, the third is the "stage" area for ceremonies or rituals or storytelling, and the fourth is for the audience – the dromos/path leads to the throne and then the observer/worshipper area. A final fifth level, the lowest level, is connected with a sizeable commanding stone entrance, now mostly collapsed and buried under trees. Cyclopean stonework is evident along the bank/mini cliff beside that entrance.

When viewed from the lower audience/worshipper level, the equinox stone figures much more prominently. Furthermore, the equinox stone has a carved slit, where an object would have likely been inserted to frame or temporarily cover the sun. I believe this could have served as a ceremony or ritual of sorts, where some disk would temporarily cover the sun as it set on the equinox stone until it was removed or broken - to reveal the sun. A sizeable vertical boulder located below the equinox stone gives it a human appearance when viewed from below. It makes me think a ritual related to the Cyclops Polyphemus may have been performed here. Polyphemus also used a boulder to enclose the cave – symbolic of an eclipse blocking the sunlight. When Odysseus and his men blinded Polyphemus, they were able to escape and see the sun again.

Currently, a large olive tree is growing between two large flat top boulders forming the "stage" area. Between the two large boulders, a wall of stones fills a gap, almost creating a giant "planter" for the tree to take root – likely its original purpose, though the current olive tree can't possibly date that far back. Nonetheless, a large tree in that same location would have been a sacred tree. The tree's location next to the podium was symbolic. The leader, officiating at the solstices and equinoxes, would have been standing next to it.

THE MYSTERY COUPLE(S) IN MINOAN GLYPTIC ART

It is interesting to note that in the divine meeting/sacred conversation motif displayed on some seal rings, we see a couple and the prominence of the male varies. Is he her son or a partner? In the Grave Circle A ring (Fig. 14), he is coming down from the sky holding a figure eight shield, and in the sacred conversation ring from the chambered tombs of Mycenae, tomb 66 (Fig. 16), it looks like he is holding a spear. Thus he must be a warrior god.

Fig. 14. Gold signet ring from Grave Circle A in Mycenae
(early 15th century BC)

The gold seal (Fig. 14) shows a more prominent woman as the sun goddess seated on stones, with female worshippers of different ages offering flowers. The sun is above the larger woman – who must be the solar deity. The moon is next to the sun and near a god holding a figure eight shield while coming down from the sky. The horizon lines function as a border between sky and scene. Trees, stones, sun, and moon are common motifs. Arthur Evans observed that the double axe represents the sun and the moon. (Marinatos, 2013, p. 32-39)

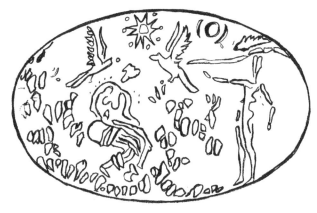

Fig. 15. Divine Couple seal ring (Poros, Crete)

The image on the Minoan gold signet ring (Fig. 15) shows the sun goddess seated on stones with the sun above her. The male deity stands below the moon with its phases and interacts with the solar goddess. The calendrical meaning of this seal ring is discussed in the next chapter.

Fig. 16. Sacred Conversation seal ring (Mycenae tomb 66)

Nanno Marinatos has interpreted this image (Fig. 16) as a couple, and the male holding the woman's wrist is making an erotic advance. Such a gesture, Marinatos states, is evident in Egyptian and later Greek art (Marinatos, 1993, p. 190). This gesture may well have been a religious motif in earlier Minoan times. I believe the elite may have had a different interpretation in Mycenae, where this ring was found.

The Homeric epics must have gone through a long evolution, and their roots may have gone as far back as Minoan times. Suppose the pre-Homeric Odysseus myth was already known in the Greek world during the Late Helladic. In that case, I suspect many Mycenaeans would have interpreted this couple as Telemachus (*Odyssey*, 1.356-359) challenging his mother's authority. He is holding a spear which can be construed as his role as protector of the city. Penelope does not assert her authority in *The Odyssey* during that episode, but the woman in the above seal ring seems to be admonishing the younger male. They are both vigorously pointing at each other: he is questioning her authority, and she is reasserting hers. I submit this scene is an older version of the Odyssey myth, showing us the diminishing role of the solar goddess' earthly representative (Penelope). We must not forget that the Greek-speaking Indo-Europeans who brought the Greek language along with them also brought along their dominant sky god, Zeus. He ultimately became the prominent deity.

There must have been an evolution in the religion practiced by the early Greeks, but it is difficult to ascertain how this evolution played out. We know that the Minoans and mainland natives practiced a very different religion than what we know of by the Iron Age, which is to say, the time of Homer and Hesiod.

Fig. 17. Seal ring Sacred Conversation (Ikarou St., Poros, Crete)

But the question of son or partner still lingers. I suggest it is both; it is a different god or interpretation of a myth depending on the ring. I say this because I see many similarities between the rings and the cult center at Archangelo, as well as *The Odyssey*. The cult center has boulders that likely had been used in baetyl worship, trees probably surrounded it, and there is a large stone throne. Furthermore, there is a podium for observing the solar solstices, and in the Poros seal ring (fig. 17), we see a seated female while the male is standing on a podium. Furthermore, the scenes of a reunion or argument between a pair seem similar to "meeting" motifs in *The Odyssey*.

I believe the same religion was practiced in Kefalonia and Minoan Crete. Thus, there may have been a royal couple who were the earthly representatives of the divine couple.

So an argument can be made that there is a connection between these seal rings and the older pre-Homeric *Odyssey* myth. It is not necessarily the same male on each ring but the same female. I believe that depending on the ring, the male can be a son or a partner, yet still, both warriors. In Fig. 18, we see a larger, more muscular, and dominant male than is displayed in Fig. 16. These are two different people.

Fig. 18. Seal ring from Thebes, "Holy Wedding"

In *The Odyssey*, we have two royal pairings of a man and a woman. First, we have Penelope and her son Telemachus. In Greek, Telemachus means warrior from afar, thus a spearman or archer, and we see that in Fig. 16, the young male is holding a spear. There is no sun above them. A sun on a seal ring denotes a solstice or equinox, and the solstice identifies the royal couple, Odysseus and Penelope.

The second couple, Odysseus and Penelope, meet after 19 years on the winter solstice, a sacred solar holiday. Figure 18 shows a much larger male with a broader chest and thicker arms. There is a balance between the two figures; neither overshadows the other, and thus, he is not the women's son. They are a couple, and they are Odysseus and Penelope.

Furthermore, they are both under a unique sunset, likely a solstice (winter?). There is a border/horizon beneath the sun, with 15 indentations in the border. This number seems purposeful. I believe it represents the days between a full and a new moon, which is half a lunar month.

Nanno Marinatos describes this scene (Fig. 18) as a female deity sitting on a shrine with a branch between the horns of consecration above it. (1993, p. 191) Yes, that is a Minoan interpretation, but did the mainland Greeks share that same interpretation? A shrine that the sun goddess sits on is a common motif in Minoan art. I submit that on the mainland, the motif was reinterpreted and became part of the Odyssey myth. Remember, Odysseus had built the marital bed connected to a tree that grew into the house. (Odyssey, 23.187-204) And thus, the Minoan motif of a sacred tree growing out of a shrine the solar goddess sits on becomes a tree connected to a bed that belongs to Odysseus and Penelope. Same images, different mythology.

There has been discussion regarding the male's midsection. It is generally agreed that there is a handle of a dagger protruding in front, and we see the dagger's blade behind him. Furthermore, above the handle of the dagger is a codpiece, which Marinatos (1993) describes as giving the impression that "he is almost ithyphallic" (aroused), and that impression is given because of the clothing he is wearing. However, given the seal ring's similarities to *The Odyssey*, I believe the male is aroused and has just announced his identity to his wife. The couple is Odysseus and Penelope – the original Middle Helladic myth has replaced the older Minoan couple by the Late Helladic period. (This will be discussed in greater detail in the next chapter.) We are seeing an older Minoan motif reinterpreted to match emerging Greek mythology.

Many questions remain: How long did this religion of the primary sun goddess and partner/son last before it was replaced by or more likely assimilated with the deities and myths of the early Greek speakers? When did Helios take the female goddess' place as the solar deity? When did the Indo-European "sky father," Zeus, replace her dominant position? Was a female high priestess representing the solar goddess replaced by a warrior king (Odysseus?) representing the sun when the Greek-speaking Indo-European migrants had arrived in Kefalonia?

Admittedly, my views are speculative yet based on a lot of evidence from which we can draw reasonable conclusions. We can see the same evolution and similarities between early Christian and late period Roman pagan iconography. Yes, there was a Minoan religion with a sun goddess paired with a younger god. Over time, however, the Indo-European Greek speakers assimilated with the existing population on the mainland, and the two groups became the Mycenaeans. I believe the new population outside Crete gradually reinterpreted these religious motifs and incorporated their mythologies using their gods and heroes. We see in *The Odyssey* religious elements of old (Bronze Age/Middle Helladic) to new (Iron Age/time of Homer). Odysseus became an example in the emerging Greek world of the warrior ruler that replaced the female representative of the solar goddess. His clever plan to connect himself to the sun must have been well known in the early Greek world. (More on that later.)

This change from a female solar goddess and earthly agent to a male warrior leader could have occurred in many Mycenaean centers as the role of the leader, the Wanaka, replaced the earlier, Minoan religion-based elite. In other words, there was an evolution in religion from the Minoan/Aegean female solar deity to the Greek pantheon of gods we are all familiar with, headed by the Indo-European sky-god Zeus.

Nonetheless, Minoan art was in vogue into the Late Helladic. Still, over time, the Myceneans would have reinterpreted the symbolism to support the new elites (an assimilation of locals and Greek speakers) who eventually took over the palace at Knossos centuries after fully controlling the mainland.

Let me be clear; I do not believe that the Indo-Europeans that migrated to Greece retained a separate identity throughout the Greek Bronze Age. Instead, they introduced a language and religion, not followed by all but followed by enough people to have eventually grown in acceptance.

By the late Bronze Age, the identities of Indo-European migrants and culturally Aegean/Minoan-related natives in mainland Greece would have been gone. They assimilated and became one people – the Mycenaeans, or a better term: the Ahhiyawa (Achaeans), a term used in cuneiform texts by the Hittites, which most likely described the new mainland Greeks. And so, there was one population but two religions, and by the Iron Age, the elements of the Indo-European religion became the dominant ones. Something akin to a religious reformation must have occurred gradually over time, possibly accelerating during the Bronze Age collapse when people would have been more likely to have questioned old beliefs.

We will see in the next chapter why I believe a small Bronze Age cemetery in the western periphery of the emerging Greek world shows us how this assimilation and evolution began with a Middle Helladic warlord assimilating two cultures. I conclude that this is the individual that ultimately became a solar hero in local Kefalonian folklore.

3

THE ROYAL TOMB DISCOVERED

A SOLAR INTERPRETATION OF A CEMETERY

After visually confirming two different sunsets and sunrises at the Archangelo solar cult center, I turned my attention to the Middle Bronze Age cemetery at Kangelisses Kokolata, some 700 meters WNW of the village of Kokolata and 700 meters SW of the Archangelo center. The cemetery is on a flat hilltop, or plateau, with 360 degrees of impressive views. Looking north, the bay of Argostoli is visible, and westward, the peak of the Lakithra mountain ridgeline, the highest western peak visible from Kangelisses. The tallest mountain in the Ionian, Mount Ainos, figures prominently WSW. Its commanding location suggests a new elite constructed this cemetery.

In this chapter, we will see that a lot of planning was involved in locating each grave or tomb. I have already mentioned how one cist grave marked the heliacal rising of the star Arcturus. This cemetery had a dual function.

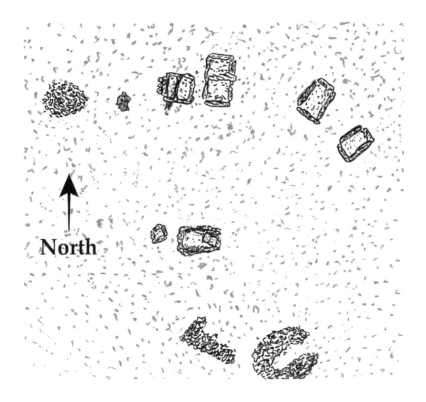

Fig. 19. Sketch of Middle Helladic Kangelisses cemetery based on Kavvadias' drawing
(Kavvadias, 1914). (I did not include the Late Helladic tombs)

The cemetery was initially constructed at the end of the Middle Helladic period between 1600 and 1550 BC. This older part of the cemetery contains six cist graves made of large stone slabs that form deep rectangles on five cists, but one is smaller and square-shaped.

During one of my trips to Kangelisses, however, I noticed a possible 7th cist grave SSW of the central cist. It does not change my analysis; if anything, it supports it, and I will discuss it later.

The central cist has an east-west orientation with a smaller one next to it, and to the north, in a radial pattern, are the remaining four cists. Stone cairns (piles of stones) served an unknown function. I think they may predate the cist graves because there is evidence (EH potsherds) that people were congregating at Kangelisses long before the Middle Helladic period.

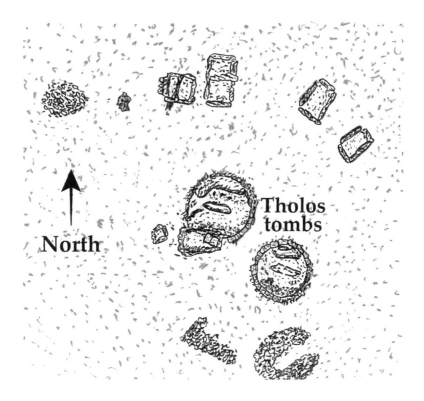

Fig. 20. Sketch based on Kavvadias' drawing, 1912, Kangelisses, Kokolata Middle Helladic cemetery with the two Late Helladic tholos tombs.

There are also two tholoi (plural of tholos) in this cemetery constructed in the Late Helladic period, around 1400 BC. A tholos tomb, also called a beehive tomb, is a deep-walled circular tomb with one or several graves inside. A tholos could also have a dromos – an opening and path that leads to it. The Minoans on Crete first used this tomb style in Greece but mainly were open, not enclosed with a dome. Most stone-domed tholos tombs were built by the Mycenaeans on the mainland and reached impressive sizes. The "Treasury of Atreus" is one such sizeable stone-domed tholos tomb. But here in Kangelisses, it seems they were not domed, and neither did they have an entrance/dromos.

I started my analysis with the site plan drawn by the Kefalonian archaeologist P. Kavvadias, who excavated the site in 1909-1912 and later in his career would excavate the ancient theater at Epidaurus.

I numbered the late Middle Helladic (circa 1600/1550 BC) cist graves 1-6 and the Late Helladic (circa 1400 BC) tholos tombs 7-8. (Fig. 21) I used simulations (Stellarium and Google Earth) to see where the sun would rise and set on solstices and equinoxes (and other celestial phenomena) when viewed from the stone slab resting on the central cist, which I previously recorded the GPS location. Sure enough, the sun's rising and setting at certain solstices, observed from the observation point, seemed to match the locations of the graves or tombs. It seemed that the stone slab may have served a purpose.

Therefore, the Late Helladic tholos tombs were also located with purpose. The accepted view is that the northern tholos was built into or around the central cist grave to show a connection, a relationship, to the older Middle Helladic individuals buried at Kangelisses. Based on the solar significance at Archangelo, my interpretation is that the tholos was also purposefully placed on the central cist to share an existing solar observation point.

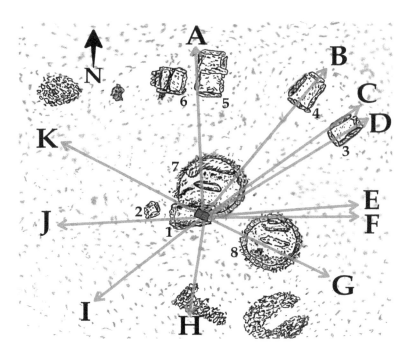

Fig. 21. Kangelisses cemetery with arrows and labels added by the author.
Observation point/slab colored red.

DECODING THE KANGELISSES CEMETERY

Mark A: Both cists (#5 and #6) cover the polar circle area, which includes the Great Bear. **Mark B:** Cist #4 marks the star Arcturus heliacal rising. **Mark C:** The width of cist #3 seems designed to mark both the major lunar standstill moonrise and **D:** the summer solstice sunrise. **Mark E:** though not marked at the cemetery, the large tholos tomb at Tzannata, Kefalonia, is located on the same latitude as Kangelisses. The tholos tomb at Tzannata seems to have been intentionally placed to share the equinox sunrise and sunset with Kangelisses (video at www.odysseus.blog). **Mark F:** the edge of tholos #8 marks the equinox as seen from Kangelisses. **Mark G:** the slab on top of cist # 1 is angularly placed to show the winter solstice sunrise (Fig. 22) and is also aligned with the Late Helladic cemetery at Mazarakata. **Mark H:** the Late Helladic cemetery at Lakithra seems to share a unique location, as does the newly discovered 7th cist grave. From Kangelisses, the constellation Argo becomes parallel with the horizon when it is above the Lakithra cemetery. **Mark I:** *nothing is marked at this location during the Middle Helladic or Late Helladic.* There is a reason for this, and we will explore it later in this chapter. **Mark J:** The edge of cist #2 marks the equinox sunset. **Mark K:** the rectangular slab's angular direction marks the summer solstice. (Fig. 22).

Fig. 22. Close-up of central cist grave/observation point at Kangelisses, Kokolata 1912. The rectangular slab is aligned with the two solstices.

For some reason, the winter solstice sunset was not marked by a grave or stone cairn at Kangelisses – neither during the Middle Helladic nor the Late Helladic periods. The cemetery is void of tombs or stone cairns in that general area. I found this very unusual because the winter solstice would have been a significant event during the Bronze Age – the beginning of the growing day: a festival of regeneration. Furthermore, this cemetery has no principal (by size or contents) grave. I looked to the horizon for clues, where the sun would set on the winter solstice, in case a natural feature stood out (Fig. 23).

Fig. 23. Photo from Kangelisses, looking west, the peak of Lakithra.

I used the planetarium software program (Stellarium), with the GPS location of the Kangelisses central cist grave with superimposed Google Earth topography of the area to see the sky as it was in 1600 BC, a round number of the currently accepted MBA period of the cemetery. Sure enough, the sun sets right into the southern slope of that peak (Fig. 24).

The photo in Fig. 24 shows the winter solstice sunset that occurs every twelve months. The number twelve, keep in mind, is frequently used in *The Odyssey*. Odysseus commanded twelve ships when he went to Troy. To win an archery competition, he shot an arrow through twelve axes (the sun passing through twelve months?). There were twelve suitors and maidens from Ithaca. These references to the number twelve in *The Odyssey* are often related to either Odysseus or Ithaca.

Fig. 24. The zoomed/cropped photo above was taken by the author at Kangelisses on December 19, 2021, two days before the winter solstice. On December 21st, the sun's location would still be in that area.

I do the same analysis from the cult center at Archangelo to look for anything unusual happening at that unique point on the horizon. Again, I recorded the GPS coordinates at the cult center at Archangelo to see the peak of Lakithra using the simulation on my computer. Above the cult center is a flat hilltop with many ancient remains.

In Fig. 25, we see the moon travel along the software's (Zotti, Archaeolines plugin) fixed green moon path of the major lunar standstill. This is the southwesternmost location the moon will ever set when viewed from Archangelo. It is the same mountain peak of Lakithra.

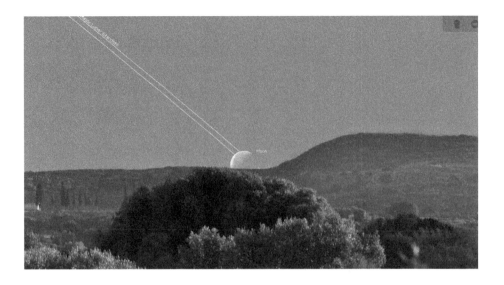

Fig. 25. Simulation: Stellarium sky/Landscape photo taken by the author.
Lunar standstill, March 21, 1605 BC, as seen from Archangelo

The sun does the same at solstices: in winter, it sets at an extreme southwestern point on the horizon, and in summer, an extreme northwestern point on the horizon. That particular moonset we see in Fig. 25 is called a major lunar standstill, an event that occurs every 18.6 years (close to the two decades Odysseus was missing from Ithaca?) when the moon sets at SW and NW extremes on the horizon. The ancients probably would not have noticed that exact date of the southwesternmost moonset because once a month, the moon would "visit" that general area on the horizon for about a year before and after the exact lunar standstill. Every subsequent moon setting in that area would incrementally change in location. Generally, the bronze age ancients would have viewed this as a two-decade phenomenon. Thus we have another coincidence. Odysseus was missing for two decades.

Before proceeding, let's review. We have a civilization at Kokolata Livatho, where the sun is viewed from one sacred site, the Kangelisses cemetery, setting near that peak every twelve months on the winter solstice. From the other sacred site, the solar cult center at Archangelo, the moon set is viewed near that same peak on the lunar solstice approximately every two decades. ***Who returned to Ithaca on the winter solstice after two decades?***

After the major lunar standstill, the moon's extreme SW and NW moonset locations will start narrowing on the horizon every month. Over time, those two extremes reach a minimum distance between a SW moon set and a NW moon set (left and right on the horizon), which is called a minor lunar standstill. (Half of 18.6 years – so 9.3 years after the major lunar standstill and then the extreme moon sets begin growing apart again until the subsequent major lunar standstill.)

That unique point on the horizon would have given an "emphasis" to what the moon was doing, and thus they would have definitely noticed it. Remember, they followed both the sun and moon as a religious exercise. These were their deities. How many people today know the sun's annual path on the horizon where they live, let alone the moon's similar path? The ancients were very different in this regard compared to us today.

I continued experimenting with dates on the Stellarium simulation I created. I noticed that four months later and a couple of days after the summer solstice, the moon would be at full phase and setting late in the night, at the same general location but closer to the area the sun sets on the winter solstice (Fig. 26).

Fig. 26. Stellarium sky/landscape photo taken from Archangelo,
full moon July 9, 1605 BC

But there's more. There is also a lunar cycle called the Metonic cycle, named after Meton of Athens, who lived in the 5th century BC. However, most scholars would conclude that this lunar cycle would have been observed by others well before Meton, likely in Mesopotamia.

The Metonic cycle occurs every nineteen years when a specific moon phase repeats. The location of the moon is against the same constellation(s). In other words, if you look at tomorrow's moon phase, even though that same moon phase will reoccur about every month, you can be sure that after nineteen years have passed, on the same day of the year, you will see that same moon phase again. For example, there was a full moon a couple of days after the summer solstice (the solstice was on a different date in the Bronze Age) on July 9, 1605 BC. (Fig. 26) Let's look at the moon again 19 years after that date (Fig. 27).

Fig. 27. Stellarium sky/landscape photo, Archangelo full moon July 9, 1586 BC

Fig. 27 shows the Lakithra peak on July 9, 1586 BC; the moon is over 99% illuminated. It is at the same location. Furthermore, this is during the summer, at a time when cloud cover is rare in Kefalonia. Thus this observation would have been highly possible. A full moon at the same location at the same time (within an hour) of the year. This specific moonset, near the time of the lunar standstill, would most likely have been noticed by the builders of the Archangelo solar cult center. Note: Early Helladic pottery sherds had been found at Kangelisses well before the construction of the Middle Helladic cemetery. It is safe to conclude that both Kangelisses and Archangelo served as areas of sun and/or moon worship, focusing on that unique point on the horizon.

Thus, this phenomenon completes a nineteen-year cycle, and we enter the twentieth year. In the twentieth year of absence from his homeland, Odysseus returned to Ithaca. Maybe they were always metaphors of the moon returning to that location after nineteen years have passed and the sun every twelve months? This analysis is not new. Many have seen a relationship between the numbers of *The Odyssey*, celestial phenomena, and calendrical units. (See in Bibliography: Papathanassiou, Wood, Murray, and for a comprehensive historical review: Guglielmino, et al.)

One more phenomenon taken right out of *The Odyssey* is more precise and must also be mentioned. Gilbert Murray, in *The Rise of the Greek Epic* (pp. 211-212, 1924 ed.), wrote as follows:

"Hence came the greatest effort of ancient calendar-making, Meton's Eikosieteris, as it was called, or Grand Eniautos of Nineteen Years. On the last day of the nineteenth year, which was also, by Greek reckoning, the first of the twentieth, the New Moon would coincide with the New Sun of the Winter Solstice; this was called the 'Meeting of Sun and Moon' (Σύνοδος Ηλιου και Σελήνης) — a thing which had not happened for nineteen full years before and would not happen again for another nineteen."

"Now when did Odysseus return to Penelope? The date is given with a precision most unusual in epic poetry. He returned to Ithaca 'just at the rising of that brightest star which heralds the light of the Daughter of Dawn' (v 93). He rejoined his wife 'on the twentieth year'; i.e., he came as soon as the twentieth year came, as soon as the nineteenth was complete (ψ 102, 170; ϱ 327, β

175). He came at the New Moon, on the day which the Athenians called 'Old-and-New', 'when one month is waning and the next rising up' (τ 307, ξ 162). This New Moon was also the day of the Apollo Feast, or Solstice festival of the sun (ν 156, φ 258), and the time was winter. The Σύνοδος Οδυσσέως και Πηνελόπης [trans: Meeting of Odysseus and Penelope] exactly coincides with the Σύνοδος of the Sun and Moon."

Regarding Murray's conclusion that it was winter, he discusses in a footnote the frequent references to the cold weather in *The Odyssey*, such as: piling up a fire, there is frost, and Odysseus freezing in his rags and cannot face the morning cold.

With this new information, I go back to my simulation and hunt for a New moon on the winter solstice.

Fig. 28. Simulation: Stellarium sky/photo topography Kangelisses
new moon and winter solstice sunset Jan. 2, 1600 BC.

Above photo: 1600 BC, new moon (highlighted, the actual moon would not be visible) at the winter solstice, view of the Lakithra Peak from Kangelisses. Using today's calendar and going back several millennia, the winter solstice would not be on December 21 as it is today. In Stellarium, I use a plugin called "archaeolines" that shows where the sun's path would be on the solstices, and I match that path with the sun, and the program gives me a date (Gregorian Calendar.)

On the same date, an hour and a half earlier, there was a partial eclipse, but unlikely to have been observed due to minimal coverage (6.99%).

Thus we also have a new moon during the winter solstice, as described by Homer for the meeting between Odysseus and Penelope. Using the Metonic cycle as a guide, we can predict that this moon phase, a New Moon, would also occur every nineteen years.

Fig. 29. Simulation: Stellarium sky/photo topography Kangelisses new moon (highlighted, top left) and winter solstice sun just before sunset. January 3, 1581 BC

Note: From my observations using Stellarium, at the completion of a Metonic cycle, the moon phase remains the same, but the moon's location can vary in relation to the horizon (though it is not visible); however, the moon's position, whether it be a full or new moon or anything in between, is always at the same location relative to the specific stars behind it (and therefore whatever constellation they form as well).

Furthermore, by observing the moon and where it sets several days before and after the new moon phase, the ancients would have had a decent estimation of its location close to the sun on this particular day. Therefore, it is highly likely that they knew both the sun and new moon set at or near that location on the horizon, or to put it differently, the two celestial bodies "met" at that mountain peak.

While experimenting on moon sets about a century before and after the Metonic cycle, I noticed a "drift" of the new moon. The moon's distance from the sun grows. This is no surprise because, at the same time, the lunar standstill process is at work which is just shy of the nineteen-year (and a day) Metonic cycle. This unique phenomenon of a new moon at the peak of Lakithra nonetheless existed well before and after the construction of the Kangelisses cemetery.

An important side note: at the end of *The Odyssey*, the Achaeans were celebrating the Festival of Apollo before Odysseus revealed his identity. (Likely the winter solstice judging by the winter clothes described by Homer) Apollo was the god of archery and, much later in ancient Greece, identified with the sun more than Helios. Nonetheless, according to Heraclitus (1ˢᵗ cent.) Homer identifies Apollo as the sun (Heraclitus, translated by Russell and Konstan, 2005, p.15).

Apollo has also been identified with amber – the tears of Apollo. Amber has been found in many Late Helladic tombs in Kefalonia. During the Late Helladic period, more Baltic amber existed in Kefalonia than in the remaining Mycenaean world. (Souyoudzoglou-Haywood 1999, pp. 84-85). It is likely that the Kefalonians, trading in amber, would have been in contact with the rest of Greece, and local Kefalonian myths would have been told during this contact. Such was one possible manner in which one region's myths spread to other areas – during trade, especially for unique objects when the buyer was just as interested in the object's provenance and chain of ownership as the object itself.

In conclusion, we have solar and lunar phenomena at the Lakithra peak that, according to my computer-generated simulations, were observable from Kangelisses and Archangelo, both sacred sites in the Bronze Age.

Before I discovered these celestial phenomena at the Lakithra peak, many past and present *Odyssey* researchers interpreted specific numbers in *The Odyssey* as the same solar and lunar phenomena from reading *The Odyssey* alone. Critics could still contend that these are mere coincidences and could have a point. (By now, you probably have an idea as to where I am going with this.) We need to take a closer look at that peak. Could there be evidence of a physical connection to *The Odyssey*? Obviously, the ancients of this area worshipped the sun and moon. But was a person somehow attached to these celestial phenomena? If so, how did he establish a connection with these solar and lunar cycles?

It was early morning when I made this discovery using Google Earth Pro. I was able to use "street view" at the Kangelisses cemetery and dated the simulation to the winter solstice to confirm where the setting sun would be on the horizon. The photo in Fig. 24 was taken after I had already made my discovery.

While viewing that horizon on Google Earth Pro, I zoomed in at that peak in Lakithra, where the solar and lunar phenomena took place as they were viewed from Archangelo and Kangelisses. I saw an unusual circular construction built into the slope of the peak. It looked like a tholos tomb. One side of a stone wall, part of the dromos/entrance extended downslope, southeast. Immediately I thought of the winter solstice sunrise. I tried a street view from above and behind the tomb. I selected December 21 as the date on the Google Earth Pro program and tilted the simulation on my screen to see the horizon opposite the tomb. There it was: the winter solstice sunrise in alignment with the dromos/entrance of what I believe is a tholos tomb.

The tomb was located at the winter solstice sunset mark on the horizon (when viewed from Kangelisses), and the tomb itself "pointed" to the winter solstice sunrise! Its elevation on that mountain, higher than any other Bronze Age tomb in the region, tells me it is a royal tholos tomb.

Locals have long considered this to be a lime kiln. However, it is much too thin and shallow, with a narrow (likely burial) shaft in the central lower area. Furthermore, I found delicate, thin reddish-orange ceramics around it, which are more likely to be found at burial sites than at a lime production area. This structure must be explored.

The initial grandee of the tomb knew what he was doing in choosing this location. This selection of tomb site is enough material proof to vindicate those who saw the astronomical and calendrical references in *The Odyssey* and, as a result, were either considered fringe theorists or ignored. There was a pre-Homeric source for these numbers. There is a reason these numbers are both relevant and indispensable to the myth, which grew out of a hero worship ritual that involved celebrating the winter solstice and a local leader. **Here lies Odysseus**. The hero cult of Odysseus took place on the feast of Apollo, that is, the winter solstice, possibly beginning at the Archangelo solar cult center, followed by a ceremonial procession to the Kangelisses cemetery to witness the winter solstice sunset at the distant royal tomb. Sun and hero became one. The initial grandee cleverly found a way to be associated with the sun on a sacred day, every year, well after his death.

Fig. 30. Royal Tholos NE view

Northeast view of the tholos. The dromos pointing southeast, to the right, is overgrown with small trees. In the top right corner, we can see the valley below, including the village of Kokolata.

Fig. 31. Royal Tholos NW view

Northwest view of the Royal Tholos. To the right is the slope of the western peak of Lakithra. The back wall of the tomb is built into the slope.

DETAILS OF THE ROYAL THOLOS

From several visits, I observed that the outside exterior ring of stones would have had a diameter of about 9 meters. The lower interior is about three meters. There is a partial "ledge" of smooth stone in the interior. I estimate there are at least 2 meters of collapsed rock. Judging from the slope of the hill and the current level of the dromos/entrance, this is a deep tholos. In the center, there seems to be a rectangular shaft, similar to the central shaft at the Tzannata tholos. The shaft here is filled with stone; no vegetation has grown from it yet, so it must be very deep. Unfortunately, given its deteriorated condition, it is highly likely to have been looted.

Fig. 32. Royal Tholos inner wall/ledge

Most stones, if not all, are unworked, save for the small area of the smooth-faced interior wall (Fig. 32). Time damage is such that it is difficult to assess if this was a domed stone tholos. Most likely, it would have been similar to the two later tholoi at Kangelisses and those of the same period and earlier found in Crete. I do not believe it had a dome, similar to other SW Kefalonia tholos tombs that also do not have a dome.

A "HINT" OF THE HERO CULT IN THE ODYSSEY?

As an aside, I want to mention a unique line in *The Odyssey* that I found most unusual. It is in Book 20, line 276:

> κήρυκες δ᾽ ἀνὰ ἄστυ θεῶν ἱερὴν ἑκατόμβην ἦγον: τοὶ δ᾽ ἀγέροντο κάρη κομόωντες Ἀχαιοὶ ἄλσος ὕπο σκιερὸν ἑκατηβόλου Ἀπόλλωνος.

"Meanwhile the heralds were leading through the city the holy hecatomb [sacrificial animals] of the gods, and the long-haired Achaeans gathered together beneath a shady grove of Apollo, the archer-god." (Homer Book 20.276 trans. A.T. Murray, 1919)

Homer described this event in The Odyssey at the same time he described Telemachus publicly insisting on where the disguised Odysseus should sit and enjoy the feast. Telemachus reminded the suitors it was his house that his father Odysseus "won" for him. The suitors were taken aback by Telemachus' newfound boldness, and the tension between the suitors and Telemachus with the disguised Odysseus escalated.

What is unusual is that the procession of the heralds with the animals to be sacrificed at the grove of Apollo (Archangelo cult center? An ancient road leads to the cult center) was a significant local event in which Telemachus and the others should have participated. Why were they still in the great hall waiting to be served? It is as if the Achaeans (Interestingly, Homer described them as "Achaeans" and not "Ithacans") were engaging in a ceremony on a feast day while a parallel story was unfolding in the house of Odysseus. The Achaeans were oblivious to what was happening in the banquet hall. Or maybe nothing was happening in that banquet hall at all?

I submit that the procession of the heralds and Achaeans with the animals to be sacrificed for the feast is a description of the hero cult celebration of Odysseus taking place. This event in the story is a "time anomaly" – *Odysseus has long been dead, and the Achaeans are celebrating him and the winter solstice sun.* This event is their hero cult ceremony taking place on the winter solstice. After the ceremony and feast at the Archangelo cult center, they will walk to see the sunset at Kangelisses, where they will watch Odysseus and the Sun "return" to Ithaca ("nostos" at the peak and his tomb). Odysseus defeats the winter just as he defeats the suitors. ***The reality: Homer described the hero cult ritual and the subsequent myth at the same time. Was Homer aware of this? Or did the description of the hero ritual somehow survive in Homer's epic?***

DATING THE ROYAL THOLOS

Middle Helladic and Late Helladic residents of the area knew of this tholos tomb because out of respect, they did not mark the winter solstice sunset with a tomb or grave at Kangelisses – neither a cist grave in the Middle Helladic nor a tholos during the Late Helladic. The winter solstice sunrise, in my view, was only marked by the angular slab atop the central cist, likely in the Middle Helladic period, and the Mazarakata cemetery, some two kilometers away, during the Late Helladic period. Thus, the royal tholos was the single grave given a unique solstice – the winter solstice, both at sunrise and sunset. The grandee buried there may not have known how his story would evolve. Still, he did cleverly realize that he would be remembered on the festival of Apollo (or whatever deity was initially celebrated on the winter solstice) when people watched that sunset from Kangelisses. He wanted immortality and succeeded, but not the way he expected.

In conclusion, this tholos tomb was likely constructed during the Middle Helladic period and possibly with continued use (and perhaps reconstruction) up to the Late Helladic period. The first grandee is a Middle Helladic warlord, a new ruler of an existing settled area, and a founder of a local religious reformation connecting himself (and most likely his wife) to the Sun and Moon. He replaced the old system yet retained many elements of the pre-existing religion. A new era began, and new stories were created, evolving into legendary myths and, ultimately, an epic.

It is interesting to note that this is a tholos tomb, not a shaft or cist grave. Its Middle Helladic contemporary graves at Kangelisses are cist graves somewhat organized to give the impression of a Kurgan/tumulus cemetery of northern influence. However, this being a tholos shows a southern, Minoan influence. In the Peloponnese, tholos tombs increased in usage at the beginning of the Late Helladic period. Nonetheless, its Minoan roots show that the new elite quickly adopted elements of Greece's native Aegean/Minoan culture. Remaining artifacts in and around the tomb will be very telling when excavated.

Until it is excavated, another argument can be made that the tholos we see today is a much later construction, a "renovation" of the original tomb. Apart from size and entrance, it is similar to the two tholos tombs at Kangelisses that date to the Late Helladic period.

Fig. 33. Mt. Ainos View from Royal Tholos

The commanding view from the tholos (fig. 33). Mt. Ainos, the tallest mountain in the Ionian Sea, figures very prominently across the valley. Kokolata village is on the left in the valley below, above the stones of the tholos.

This tholos tomb's location at the highest elevation of all Bronze Age tombs in the immediate area, and I believe the entire island, with commanding views of Mount Ainos and unique solar and lunar relationships to the sacred sites of Archangelo and Kangelisses makes it the most important individual Bronze Age tomb of all Kefalonia if not all the Ionian islands. It is important to note that the island we call Ithaca today, which has been excavated and searched by archaeologists for over 200 years, does not contain a fraction of the mortuary evidence we see in the area of Argostoli-Kokolata-Livatho. Not even one royal tholos tomb, or any size tholos tomb, has been found on today's Ithaca.

KANGELISSES – TUMULUS OR NOT?

There is uncertainty as to if the Kangelisses cemetery was a tumulus: a burial of one or more individuals close to each other, covered by a large earthen mound. This type of cemetery or burial can be found in mainland Greece (not Crete) to Epirus up to Albania (Oikonomidis, et al. 2011), with roots going back to the Yamnaya migration from the Pontic-Caspian steppes. Archaeologist Marija Gimbutas used the term "Kurgan," which initially described this burial style for her "Kurgan Hypothesis" (the Indo-European migration from north of the Black Sea to most of Europe. The issue in identifying if the Kangelisses cemetery was a tumulus is that much of the earthen mound if it existed at all, is not present. Yet the cist graves were arranged as if a round earthen mound covered them.

I submit it is a hybrid cemetery. There was assimilation between two culturally different groups. Kurgan tumulus meets Minoan peak (nature) sanctuary. It resembles a tumulus in terms of a radial pattern in a slightly elevated naturally formed circular area but functions as a Minoan peak sanctuary using the flat hilltop's elevation for solar, lunar, and stellar observances. I do not believe it could have been a conventional tumulus, as a large earthen mound would have obstructed the viewing of its solar marks, the cist graves. The non-Greek speaking natives in the Early Helladic period most likely "discovered" the unique winter solstice view of Lakithra from Kangelisses, which shared the lunar standstill viewed from their solar cult center at Archangelo. It was always a sacred site, even before the Kangelisses cemetery was built.

I would like to note that I am investigating the phenomenon of the tumulus of western Greece and southern Albania, likely burial designs inspired by the Indo-European Kurgan. From the sketches made by archaeologists, I have not seen one yet that could act as a solar calendar/observatory. Something unique had happened at Kangelisses: an assimilation or adoption of ideas between newcomers and natives expressed in a cemetery.

Kefalonia, being on the periphery of the Mycenaean world, retained much of the older pre-Indo European local religion and incorporated elements of it into its myths and civilization. The Indo-Europeans that migrated to the island adapted to the local customs. It could be described as Indo-European Greek speakers (with a patriarchal sky god) met (Neolithic) Anatolian farmer migrants with an Aegean female solar-based religion. Kangelisses represents this assimilation: part Kurgan migrant tumulus style cemetery with centrally located cist graves, part Cretan-influenced open-air peak sanctuary in function, not necessarily style, for marking solstices and the star Arcturus. (For further information on certain Minoan peak sanctuaries, see: Blomberg and Henriksson, 1997.)

I believe the Western Greek tribes that were migrating southwards (including the Kephallenian) would have at one point been in the area of south Albania/North Macedonia, which in turn, was influenced by Dalmatia and the East Adriatic coast, which Volker has described as "a large tumuli province." (Volker, 2012, p. 547)

The solar cult center at Archangelo Kokolata, older than Kangelisses, has characteristics found on Minoan seal ring motifs: trees and boulders (baetyls) that worshippers used to interact with the deities. Thus, it seems that Odysseus and subsequent leaders may have replaced the prior religion's female representative of the solar deity but maintained elements of the local solar religion. It was a gradual process, and we don't know how the assimilation first began. The Homeric epics were written centuries later and give us a very different picture of religion than the first Greeks likely practiced in Greece. We only see hints of the older religion in iconography and Linear B tablets that have been translated. Admittedly, this is speculation on my part.

Although the cemetery of Kangelisses is not structurally an imposing cemetery such as the contemporary Grave Circle B at Mycenae, it is located on a flat peak with commanding views. Its location and function, not construction, gave it significance. It symbolized the dawn of the Greeks in this part of Greece and greatly influenced the island until the Late Helladic period. The Late Helladic population greatly respected Kangelisses and the people who created it and were buried there.

At the cemetery of Kangelisses, some individuals were buried in pit graves carved into the exposed rock and naturally existing crevices. These were Late Helladic period burials with valuable objects, including seal stones. It seems that for many elite Late Helladic era Kefalonians, it was better to be buried in a carved rock pit or crevice at the much older Kangelisses cemetery rather than at a more "modern" period chamber tomb at Mazarakata or even Lakithra - a cemetery of chamber tombs for the wealthy. Why? Kangelisses was considered most sacred – the people buried in rock crevices were near their ancient heroes of the Middle Helladic period with a view of the winter solstice sun at the royal tholos. It was a privilege reserved for only a few. Furthermore, I would like to mention again that the "kingly looking" tholos tomb at Tzannata in southern Kefalonia is aligned with the cemetery at Kangelisses – they used the equinox sunrise and sunset viewed from Mount Ainos to determine its location.

I would further submit that the stone material used for the cist graves at Kangelisses was likely carved and transported from the geological phenomenon around the Archangelo solar cult center, a hillside area over 70 meters long of massive cascading boulders. I have seen similar slabs in the general area of Archangelo, whose purpose is unclear. Thus, it is not illogical to conclude that some stone worship/ceremonies also took place at Kangelisses.

INTERPRETATIONS OF MINOAN GLYPTIC ART AND ARCHITECTURE BASED ON ARCHAEOASTRONOMY ARE CRUCIAL FOR INSIGHT

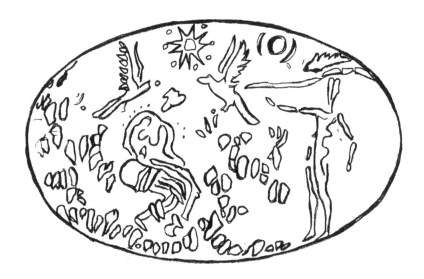

Fig. 34. Divine Couple seal ring (Poros, Heraklion)

In the above Minoan seal ring, which I reviewed in the chapter analyzing the Archangelo solar cult center, we see various elements that apply to the tomb's relation to the solstice and moon. The tomb's initial grandee and likely wife were possibly the earthly representatives of the sun and moon. *The Odyssey* also holds these clues in its solar and lunar allegories. There seems to have been a "Minoanisation" of Kefalonia centuries before the cultural influences of the Peloponnese (Mycenaeanisation) reached Kefalonia. In the interim, a unique local culture evolved with the arrival of Indo-Europeans. It was a blend of the Minoan and the Indo-European.

The Divine Couple seal ring (Fig. 34), according to Rethemiotakis (2016, p. 14), with its moon phases, explicitly shows the measurement of the month. Rethemiotakis further states: "the duration of the lunar month for the Minoans is marked by the appearance and disappearance of the moon [the new moon] in the night sky with the middle of the month falling exactly on the day of the full moon." He also concludes that the sun likely represents an annual event: an equinox or a solstice. This signet ring, therefore, represents the origin of the Minoan calendar. I will add: doesn't *The Odyssey* do the same through solar and lunar allegories? More on the calendrical allegories found in the Odyssey will be analyzed later.

Furthermore, in my view, seeing the image on the seal ring in its entirety, one cannot avoid recalling Murray's "Meeting of Sun and Moon/ Σύνοδος Ηλιου και Σελήνης" as corresponding to the meeting of Penelope and Odysseus. The image of a reunion of a man and woman at a unique solar solstice and moon phase is explicit in *The Odyssey*, as Murray concluded, and could also be interpreted in the seal ring of the Divine Couple and again at the location of the royal tholos when viewed from Kangelisses: where there is the winter solstice sunset, and at the end of nineteen years, beginning on the first day of the twentieth year, there is a new moon on that specific winter solstice. That lunar cycle always repeats, even today.

But unlike most Minoan art depicting a primary solar goddess, *The Odyssey* is very male-centric and patriarchal. Here, one is only limited to their imagination as to what transpired for there to be a new elite that constructed the Kurgan-like Kangelisses cemetery and who they were. We can then imagine many scenarios involving the rise of Odysseus as the new local chieftain. An example could be that the real Penelope may have been from a local elite non-Greek family. Maybe the archery competition in *The Odyssey* (which has similarities with the Mahabharata epic discussed in the final chapter) was a different story in the deep past, a story about how Odysseus actually "won" Penelope's hand in marriage and over time, during the Mycenaeanisation of the island, her genealogy was changed. In ancient Greece, changes in the genealogy of heroes were common. As a past hero's fame rose, for political influence, other cities, for example, would change the hero's genealogy from the other area to establish a "connection" to this outside hero and, thus, a connection to a different city or region. One such myth involves Sysiphus (a Corinthian King) that seduced Anticleia, mother of Odysseus, which makes Sysiphus the birth father of Odysseus and not Laertes, as told in *The Odyssey*.

THE MEETINGS/ΣΥΝΟΔΟΙ: ODYSSEUS AND PENELOPE, THE DIVINE COUPLE, THE SUN AND MOON OVER THE TOMB

Fig. 35. Odysseus speaks to Penelope. Source: *Das Homer-Zimmer für den Herzog von Oldenburg. Ein klassizistisches Bildprogramm des "Goethe-Tischbein"*, ed. Alexandra Sucrow and Peter Reindl (Oldenburg: Landesmuseum, 1994), p. 20. Photographed by H. R. Wacker. Scanned by James Steakley, Wikimedia.

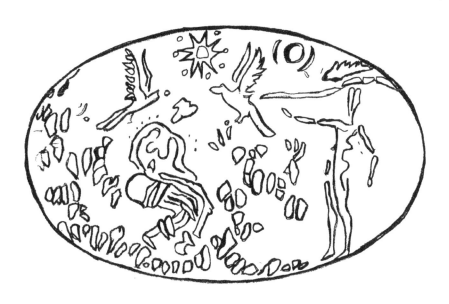

Fig. 36. Divine Couple seal ring (Poros, Heraklion)

The Divine Couple Seal Ring. The meeting of a couple and the meeting of the sun and moon – are common religious motifs shared by this ring and *The Odyssey*. Below, in Fig. 37, we see the reality behind the Odyssey and the Minoan motif of the reunited couple.

Fig. 37. Stellarium sky/Photo of Lakithra Peak winter solstice sunset and a simultaneous new moon above the royal tholos, Jan. 2, 1600 BC.

In the chapter on constellations, I review the various constellations that "interact" with the royal tholos. However, for now, I want to bring up another interpretation of Orion's constellation and the star Sirius mentioned in other contexts by Rethemiotakis (2016, p. 25) and the coauthors Blomberg and Henriksson (2014, p. 1440.)

Fig. 38. Stellarium sky/ double axe constellation over royal tholos

The main stars of the Constellation Orion and the star Sirius (part of Canis Major) form a double axe and pass over the royal tholos before setting. (Fig. 38) In the early hours before dawn, in the late autumn and winter months during the seventeenth and sixteenth centuries BC, the double axe ("the most important Minoan symbol" - Blomberg and Henriksson, 2014) passes just over the royal tholos and sets. This constellation would have been noticed, giving that location an additional value as a sacred site.

One more observation on the Kangelisses cemetery: at the beginning of this chapter, I numbered the cist graves 1-6. These numbers were also chosen to illustrate a possible ranking of the importance of the cist graves. Number 1 is the observation point, and #2 is next to it but was not a full cist for some reason. Number 3 is the solar sunrise, and on. (See diagram on page 14.) The observation point/cist #1 would be the most important, possibly a religious figure that served the leader who may have also been responsible for observing and declaring the sun's movements. The least significant would be the pair below the northern constellations/polar circle.

Fig. 39. Photo, Kangelisses, summer solstice sunrise over cist grave,
June 21, 2022.

Fig. 39, Kangelisses, east view: the photo was taken from above the observation point over the central cist grave. Beneath the sunrise lies cist grave #1 – purposefully positioned to mark the summer solstice. In 1600-1550 BC, the sun would have been to the left by about one sun width.

SEAL RINGS AND THE HOMERIC EPICS

As mentioned in the previous chapter, several Minoan seal/signet rings with common motifs (divine couple, sun, moon, and warrior) give us a picture of a religion we see elements of in *The Odyssey*. What about *The Iliad*?

There is another common motif on seal rings from the Peloponnese and Crete. In this motif, we have two men engaged in mortal combat. Many have noted that these signet rings, found in tombs of various centers on the Peloponnese and Crete, may have represented a shared legend or story familiar to these Mycenaean centers. Each area's rings could have portrayed the local warrior hero in battle, and since these motifs are common to these centers, there may have been a related myth based on a war connecting these centers. Some have hypothesized that in these rings, we could see the beginning of the myth that ultimately evolved into the epic we know as the *Iliad*. (Lewartowski, 2019)

This interpretation would not be much different than what I am proposing with my understanding of the divine couple ring and other "sacred conversation" rings. These images on seal rings dated between 1500-1350 BC, with similar motifs, told stories. The elite Minoans or Mycenaeans that commissioned these works of art, as far as we know, did not have a written tradition in storytelling but an oral one. Thus objects of art likely illustrated and archived these stories. This interpretation based on glyptic art further shows that the Homeric epics have much deeper historical roots, older than the palatial period. These seal rings represent the individuals of hero myths that ultimately became epics.

DECEMBER 19TH, 2021:

Fig. 40. Photo, near winter solstice at Kangelisses. The cist grave in the foreground was the observation point.

There were few clouds that Sunday afternoon, so I went to Kangelisses to observe the sunset a couple of days before the winter solstice, not wanting to risk a cloudy day on the actual solstice. The sunset location would have minimally changed on the actual winter solstice. This is the photo I took. I was standing behind the cist grave that also functions as the observation point for solstices. The sun is setting right at the royal tholos – **Odysseus as the sun**, the twelfth month of the year, marking an ancient year-end festival and the end of my odyssey that led me to Odysseus. I felt a sense of awe when I witnessed this. No one else had understood this solstice for probably three millennia.

Nostos of the sun, Odysseus returns. The sun sets in the area of the tholos for almost two weeks. The Lunar calendar was short around that equal amount of time at year's end, so the duration of the sun's location there could have marked the festival of Apollo that possibly added the remaining days of the solar year.

I had mentioned before the central cist grave at Kangelisses, and this warrants further analysis, especially if the structure I identify as a tholos tomb is something else. Initially, not much significance had been assigned to the central cist grave based on its size and common contents with the other graves. However, now that we know it functioned as the central solar observation point, it is not illogical to conclude that it likely was the burial of a priest that presided over solar ceremonies. The small cist next to it contained a tinned bronze knife that may have been used for sacrifices. This further strengthens the argument that it was a high priest or priestess.

I submit that if the structure at the peak is not a tomb, then the first person buried at that central cist grave was a priest-king/leader that subsequent folklore turned into the solar hero who eventually became the character in *The Odyssey*. Nonetheless, I strongly believe in my first theory and that the person buried at the central cist was most likely of the original solar worshipping natives. And so, we have a cemetery combing two cultures and two important individuals that helped assimilate two groups: a priest/ess at the central cist grave at Kangelisses, and a leader/warlord at the tholos tomb at the peak, where the winter solstice sun sets, which I will later identify as the true "Ithaca."

4

HOMERIC WORDPLAY

ODYSSEUS: A NAME WITH MORE THAN ONE MEANING

The goddess Dysis (η Δύσις) was one of the twelve Horae, all daughters of the sun god Helios or god of time, Kronos, depending on the source. She represented the sunset (το ηλιοβασίλεμα). (Unfortunately, the available literature is unclear about when she was initially worshipped.)

If unique sunsets at Archangelo were celebrated while the sun set behind the leader as he stood on the podium, we might have a connection with the goddess Dysis. The same connection can be inferred from the winter solstice sun setting at the royal tomb. Thus it is possible leaders of this region had a title: "Ο Δυς" - *The West One* – a masculine form of the name of the goddess Dysis. To summarize, the root word dys/δυς is a verb as in: "the sun sets" = "ο ήλιος δύει," and in addition to that, it also means "west."

To break it down, we have the male definite article "ο," the root Dys for the noun "west" or verb "to set," and a name ending "-eus," thus: O-dyss-eus. Was this title always "Ο Δυς/ Δυσσευς ?" or was it something else initially, later translated to the name we know today? Linguists will know better. I believe Homer knew this but played with words as all talented storytellers do. After all, "δυς "is also a root word with a negative connotation such as "difficulty/ δυσκολία," thus, the "one who suffers" as Homer described Odysseus - a brilliant pun. Homer uses both meanings of the root word "δυς"; for example, the greek phrase in *The Odyssey*: "δύσετό τ᾽ ἠέλιος" (*Odyssey* 3.487, 497) is "the sun set."

PRECEDENCE FOR A ROYAL TITLE BASED ON THE CELESTIAL SPHERE AND THE WESTERN "EDGE" OF CIVILIZATION

This would not be the first time a leader has had a title related to the sky. Some scholars have concluded that the word "Minos" eventually became the title of the ruler of Knossos. American philologist David Adams Leeming (2003) suggests that the name "Minos" could have its roots in the word for "moon." In *The Iliad*, Homer refers to the moon as "μήνης," which gave the name to the word "month/μήνας" because the cycle of the moon is what was used to count a month. (Indo-European examples: English: Month/Moon, Deutsche: Monat/Mond.) That title was likely used from 2000 B.C. and after. This would be a reasonable interpretation because, in Minoan glyptic art that shows the moon, a male is near or beneath it, whereas the sun is above the female. Many identify her as a solar goddess. On the other hand, Odysseus may have cleverly chosen "Δυς," which is unrelated to any particular celestial object. In so doing, he captured constellations, the sun, and the moon, which all *set* in the *west,* plus Odysseus was the westernmost leader of the Greek world.

Written sources in Bronze Age Greece are limited to linear B tablets used for accounting purposes; unfortunately, they give us a limited view of their civilization. In the east, however, the situation was different; we have many written sources covering many topics. For example, we know from written sources that Crete was called "Kaphtor" or "Kaptaru" by the Egyptians and the inhabitants of the Syro-Palestinian coast. I bring this up because Nanno Marinatos' description of how eastern civilizations viewed Crete as the edge of the civilized world has, in my mind, a similarity to *The Odyssey*. Marinatos states:

> "In Ugaritic myths, Crete is the kingdom of the craftsman god Kothar-and-hasis, and Kaphtor (kptr) is referred to as "the seat of his dwelling." "Shapsh, . . . carry my voice to Kothar-and-Hasis in Crete (kptr),' we read in an Ugaritic prayer.

This last information comes as a surprise: who is this Ugaritic god with a double name and why is he associated with Crete? It is often stressed that he was a god of crafts. It is less known that he was also a pilot of the sun goddess Shapsh(u), ferrying her back to the netherworld. That a deity of transition to the beyond had his residence in Crete is not without significance and suggests that Ugaritic peoples perceived the island as the land of the setting sun in the far west. To this effect, a passage in an Egyptian papyrus' "as far as the Keftiu,' lends its support. Crete was thus considered to be close to the edges of the civilized world in the west, a land close to the gods and the setting sun." (Marinatos, 2010, p.1-2)

The similarity here is that the homeland of Odysseus is also considered the western edge of the Greek world. The western edge of any civilization thus is significant in a solar sense because that is where the sun sets, and *The Odyssey* is riddled with solar metaphors. In addition, descriptions of Odysseus' travels in the west paint a picture of an uncivilized region, just as the Egyptians viewed anything beyond Crete. Furthermore, the royal tomb is also at the western edge of the Kokolata-Livatho area, on an elevated ridgeline where the sun and moon set. And so, we return to Odysseus' name as the "**West One**," the leader of the largest western settlement in the Greek world.

In Homer's *Odyssey*, Book 9, lines 25-26, Odysseus claims, "Ithaca itself lies close in to the mainland the furthest toward the gloom, but the others lie apart toward the Dawn and the sun…" (Odyssey, trans. Murray, 1919) Many, including Bittlestone and Professor Diggle (Bittlestone et al., 2005), interpret this phrase to mean that Ithaca must lie west and the modern Ithaca does not. Therefore, it must be Kefalonia, which lies west, and in particular, the Paliki peninsula, which may have been a separate island.

Whether Paliki was ever a separate island merely 4000 years ago is controversial and yet to be proven. Furthermore, many have insisted on this interpretation regardless of Paliki ever being a separate island.

My point is that if Ugarit and Egypt considered Crete the western edge of civilization, they surely meant Knossos, the largest settlement in *central* Crete, not the specific western coast of Crete, the island. The same holds for Kefalonia. We can't look to Kefalonia's western coast for Odysseus' homeland. Kefalonia, the westernmost island in the central Ionian, satisfies that requirement. Therefore, we need to find the most populated area of Kefalonia. We already know it from two hundred years of archaeological excavation. It is Kokolata-Livatho. No other region in Kefalonia comes close.

EVOLUTION OF THE WORD "BASILEUS," BOTH VERB AND NOUN

In *The Odyssey*, after the slaughter of the suitors, many of their relatives wanted to exact revenge on Odysseus. Athena implored Zeus for help in ending the bloodshed. He decreed that wealth and peace should come to the land and (according to many translations of *The Odyssey*) that Odysseus *should be ruler for life*. This interpretation, however, is a misreading and an incorrect translation.

Zeus actually said that Odysseus "*will be ruler forever* "(βασιλευέτω αἰεί, 24.483). But this is impossible for a mortal. What did Homer or the original myth mean by forever? We have an answer if we consider this newly discovered tholos tomb at the peak of Lakithra, which to this day, the sun sets on every winter solstice, the meaning "rule forever" becomes more evident.

Zeus' words were indeed correct. In Greek, there is a phrase about the sun: "ο ἥλιος βασιλεύει" – which if literally translated means "the sun rules/reigns," but in Greek, it means "the sun sets." The verb "to rule" is also used to indicate "to set" when the subject of the verb "to rule" is the sun. The use of "set" is a pun describing the winter solstice sunset at the final resting place of Odysseus. We now know that the sun will always set on the tomb of Odysseus every twelve months. It still does today.

Furthermore, we can also interpret the phrase "*will be ruler forever* "as Zeus' support of a specific patriarchal line of succession, and here, the title ¨Ο Δυς/The West One¨ will continue as well – beyond the original Odysseus.

Suppose this small part of *The Odyssey* was pre-Homeric (part of the original myth). In that case, we see a significant step in the evolution of the religion practiced in the Greek world from a primary solar goddess to an Indo-European patriarchal sky god type religion.

The Solar goddess and her earthly representative diminished in power, and eventually, the roles ceased to exist. Odysseus replaced the earthly representative of the sun goddess, and Zeus eventually became the new supreme god.

Nonetheless, women and goddesses retained their significance in the early Greek world. Compared to other female characters in Greek mythology, Penelope is a mortal female with agency - a unique strong-willed character in her own right, irrespective of gender.

The influential woman that managed an estate or administrative center was a familiar figure in Minoan Crete. Crete, a significant island of many centers that ruled the sea, called in Greek a thalassocracy, would have had many men on sea voyages for a substantial part of the year. Women naturally would have assumed many vital responsibilities in their husbands' absence, giving them a permanent civic significance. We see this in Minoan Art, where women are depicted as equal or even more important than men. In *The Odyssey*, Penelope, during Odysseus' absence, was no stranger to such responsibilities while raising her child alone.

THE SUN KING REIGNS

During the Bronze Age collapse in Greece, the ruler called "Wanax" and the second in command, "Lawegetas," the plausible title of the army commander, were likely both overthrown as the palaces burned. It is possible that the holder of the title "basileus" (linear B: qa-si-re-u), a likely third in command, or leaders of economic units such as bronzesmiths, may have assumed a leadership role during the political vacuum that followed.

In Homer's time, the word βασιλευς/basileus meant "king" as it does today, and the verb form "to rule/reign" as well as "to set" when the subject is the sun.

But it was not likely to have had that "kingly" meaning before the collapse since that title holder was third in command at best. If the basileus indeed became the new ruler, he would have needed to establish a connection to the sun for legitimacy. The meaning of "basileus" evolved into the more powerful word "king." Parallel to that change, the verb form now had a dual connotation: "to rule" as in a king rules, and "to set" as in the sun sets: the King rules so long as the sun sets.

NOSTOS: ODYSSEUS AND THE SUN RETURN

When the disguised Odysseus returned to Ithaca and first introduced himself to his unknowing wife, he said his name was Aithon. The greek meaning of this term, "αἴθων/ aithon," is "burning/blazing." (Levaniouk, 2011) We can interpret this as his wanting revenge on the suitors and burning desire to be with his wife. However, remember this is also a story about a solar-based religion. What else burns and blazes? The sun. Odysseus just announced the sun had returned "home." Literary creativity aside, in reality, the sun returns to the tomb on the winter solstice. Odysseus' return to Ithaca is a metaphor for the sun's return to the royal tholos at Lakithra on the winter solstice: the same sunset that had been worshipped at Kangelisses well before the arrival of the Greeks on Kefalonia.

"ITHACA"

Most important of all however, is the term "Ithaca." As mentioned in the beginning of this book, countless archaeologists have searched the island we call Ithaca today with discouraging results. What if Ithaca was never a place name, but a description of a topographical feature? The two greek root words that form the word "Ithaca" are Ἰθύς and Ἀκή. Together these two terms can be interpreted to mean "a guiding peak." Thus Ithaca itself may have been an actual description of a peak where the sun set on an important solstice when viewed from a sacred area. Here we see the importance of the Kangelisses cemetery as a solar cult and the peak across that "guides." More on this in the conclusion of this book. Furthermore, on my blog I have recently posted an article where I analyze Egyptian mythology and trace solar worship of mountain peaks from the Egytpian goddess Hathor, to the Egyptian symbol for the horizon, then on to the Minoan bull motif and horns of consecration which concludes with the peak across from Kangelisses. (See: www.odysseusfound.blog)

5

THE NIGHT SKY: THE STORY OF ODYSSEUS UNFOLDS

A NOTE ON THE IMAGES THAT FOLLOW

The following images of constellations are from two sources in Stellarium open-source planetarium (http://stellarium.org). The artistic renditions (Stellarium, contributing artist Johan Meuris: https://johanmeuris.eu) are based on the currently accepted Western Constellations. Unless otherwise noted, sky simulation images that follow are from early November to the winter solstice, end of Middle Helladic to Late Helladic.

The constellations without artistic interpretations that follow are the constellations from the *Almagest* of Claudius Ptolemy (sky culture was compiled and added to Stellarium by Alina Schmidt, Lea Jabschinski, Marie von Seggern, and Susanne M. Hoffmann.)

The *Almagest* of Claudius Ptolemy was the first published summary of the ancient heavens, around 150 AD. However, as I will discuss later in this chapter, many constellations probably have their roots in Minoan times and beyond.

THE OLDEST STORY EVER TOLD? THE COSMIC HUNT
(see: Julien d'Huy, 2016)

Before continuing, we must first delve deep into history - the Paleolithic period.

There is a story, taking various forms, that has been told worldwide - from the Iroquois in North America to the Chutsky in Siberia, including the Proto Indo Europeans, Africans, and Asians. It is the story of the cosmic hunt.

The story involves a hunter or hunters, and usually a bear or a moose/deer, depending on the story's area. As the prey is injured, it continues to flee from its hunters until it reaches the horizon. The prey escapes its hunters, becoming a constellation, and in some stories, the hunter(s) do the same. Depending on the story, the constellations involved are usually the Big Dipper and Orion. In later Greek mythology, Callisto, who had been turned into a bear by the goddess Artemis, was almost hunted down by her unknowing son Arcas. At the last minute, Zeus saved her by turning her into the Bear constellation.

The horizon plays an essential role in many versions of the myth. It is also crucial for the location of the royal tholos tomb. This story also likely inspired the selection of the royal tomb's location.

Perhaps the phrases <οἶνοψ πόντος> wine-dark sea and <ῥοδοδάκτυλος Ἠώς> rosy-fingered dawn were the beginning and the end of the nightly observation of the sky that provided the ancients with "miraculous" material and inspiration for creating myths. The night sky was their "big screen," and they watched it as long as the weather permitted. Their frequent observances of the night sky made them familiar with the stars, a familiarity now lost to modern people. In addition, the low light pollution of the Bronze Age must have made the night sky look spectacular. If the daytime views from Kangelisses are magnificent, the nighttime sky, viewed from Kangelisses with a unique 360-degree elevated horizon, provided views of horizons of various mountains that gave context to the constellations they followed. The stars, the constellations, and the nighttime moon all interacted with the horizon and the royal tholos.

Much has been said about the often used phrase "wine-dark sea," and I have an interpretation. Ancient societies were largely agrarian societies. Even those not engaged in farming, for example, bards, were familiar with the process, including the processing and storage of wine. One can imagine looking down into a large deep pithos of wine; no matter the color of the wine, the liquid would be dark due to the depth of the pithos and because the ceramic material of the pithos blocks the light. Specks of dust and debris floating on the surface would mimic stars. That, to me, would have been the origin of the "wine dark sea" - the starry night

THE CONSTELLATIONS TELL A STORY

I will begin by showing images of various constellations and their unique positions on the horizon as viewed from ancient Kangelisses. I chose November-December circa 1600 BC for all these images. These constellations would be in the same positions more or less for the next few centuries. That is, the change in the earth's axis would not have significantly affected these images in relation to the horizon for the rest of the Bronze Age.

Fig. 41. Stellarium sky/Google Earth topography view from Kangelisses, Orion rises over Mt. Ainos

From July until mid-November, at different night hours, depending on the month and day, we see the impressive constellation Orion rising out of Mt. Ainos, the tallest mountain in the Ionian Sea. Given its height, this mountain was considered sacred, and many have considered it to be the original Mt. Neriton that Odysseus speaks proudly of.

Fig. 42. Stellarium sky/Landscape photo taken by the author at Kangelisses,
Boötes stands over Argostoli Bay

As Orion and Taurus rise from Mt. Ainos, the constellation Boötes, also mentioned in
The Odyssey, stands above the bay of Argostoli, one of the most sheltered, calm bays in the
Mediterranean. During the winter months in Kefalonia, I have seen many ships ride out
storms anchored in Argostoli Bay.

Although Orion rises from Mt. Ainos, it travels in the night sky for several hours, then
passes just above the royal tholos and sets. The ship Argo, a southern constellation, rotates
in a tighter circle, dipping beneath the horizon just as its bow reaches the royal tholos
seen from Kangelisses. Canis Major, the dog called "Kyon" in ancient Greek, follows.

Fig. 43. Stellarium sky/Landscape photo from Kangelisses, Western constellations:
Puppis (formerly Argo), Canis Major, Orion, and Taurus.

Fig. 44. Stellarium sky/Landscape photo from Kangelisses, Almagest constellations:
Argo (ship) – Kyon (dog) – Orion (hunter) – Taurus (bull).
Lagos, the hare, is seen setting into the horizon. Images from *The Odyssey*.

Two coincidences: Odysseus' dog is named Argos, like the ship constellation next to Canis Major/Kyon, the dog constellation. Is that how the creator(s) of the Odysseus myth came up with that name? Odysseus' dog Argo had also waited two decades to see his master again. Just by smell, the frail aging dog realized his disguised owner had returned, wagged his tail, and passed away. The disguised and emotional Odysseus turned his head to hide his tear, not wanting to be known.

Taurus' horns point to the hunter Orion - as if he were going to be injured. In *The Odyssey*, we learn that in his youth, Odysseus was wounded by a boar's tusk while hunting. The injury had left a scar on his leg that gave away his identity to the only person that recognized him despite his disguise: Eurycleia, his aging nanny that helped raise him. And so, twice in *The Odyssey*, we see Odysseus' disguise fail him – both stories inspired by the constellations over the tomb seen from Kangelisses. I believe the ancients used these constellations not just for the story but also as clues to identify this tomb as the tomb of Odysseus.

We can surmise that people at Kangelisses were observing these constellations passing over the royal tholos and got ideas from them. These night sky observations show how parts of myths were created: loosely based on a person's actual life, older stories, and elements inspired by observing the night sky woven into the story. These are pieces of the pre-Homeric *Odyssey*.

Note that the older ancient Greek constellation Argo is not called such today. Due to its size and amount of stars within it, it was broken up into three constellations in 1763: Carina, the keel, Puppis, the poop deck or stern, and Vela, the sails.

The Lakithra cemetery of chamber tombs, which had bronze weapons, gold, and Italian objects, could have housed the burials of seafaring warriors who had traveled west. Quite a few of those buried at Lakithra had injuries on the left side of the head, indicating hand-to-hand combat. (Metaxas, 2022) Therefore, its location under the constellation Argo of Jason and the Argonauts may have been intentional. Although that constellation in the Bronze Age was higher on the horizon and traveled SE to SW, it is when it is nearly parallel to the horizon, approaching the royal tholos, that it passes over the Lakithra cemetery. To the right of the Lakithra cemetery, further along, the ridgeline of Lakithra, and just before its peak, is the royal tholos. The ship Argo sets into the tomb.

Fig. 45. Dawn. Stellarium sky/landscape photograph of the southwestern view from Kangelisses.
Almagest constellation Kyon "the dog" and the ship Argo approaching the tomb.
The star Sirius is still visible at dawn and fades as it passes over the royal tomb.

In early November, if we look at the Lakithra horizon an hour before sunrise, the star Sirius, part of the constellation Canis Major, in ancient times called Kyon, "the dog" (Odysseus' dog Argo?), passes over the royal tholos and fades. (Fig. 45) The setting of a star at dawn is also called a cosmic setting when a star sets and is still briefly visible in the morning twilight. To the observers at Kangelisses, Argo, Odysseus' loyal canine companion, dies/fades with that star and constellation. Most likely, this was an important date on their calendar as it took place two months before the winter solstice.

Another snippet of *The Odyssey*? If Canis Major/Kyon was given the name "Argo" from the constellation Argo next to it and fades/dies as it "meets" the royal tholos – was this the inspiration for the last meeting between Odysseus and his dog? My blog (www.odysseusfound.blog) has a list of video links, including a 180-degree video simulation of the constellations Orion and Taurus rising from Mt. Ainos, the dog and the ship Argo following behind, and the dog ultimately fading away as he reaches the royal tomb.

Dogs figure prominently in proto-Indo-European culture. (Anthony, 2007) There are frequent references to the proto Indo-European view of dogs and death, sacrifice rituals of dogs and wolves at the winter solstice.) Marija Gimbutas had also written about dogs and death, but regarding Neolithic Europe, where dogs accompanied the goddess of death and regeneration. (Gimbutas, 1999, p. 110) The concept of regeneration could also be seen in the celebration of the winter solstice when days begin to grow longer.

The scene of Odysseus' dog Argo dying was an emotional moment for both the audience listening to the bard telling the story and, of course, Odysseus, the protagonist. However, there is more to it. Argos' death is also a regenerative motif signaling the upcoming winter solstice and the rebirth – the beginning of the growing day- and an omen of what was to occur to the suitors.

In *The Odyssey*, there is one more reference to a dog. When the disguised Odysseus returned to Ithaca, he told his wife Penelope that he had met Odysseus in Crete. Penelope then asked this "stranger" what Odysseus was wearing when he was in Crete. The disguised Odysseus mentioned a cloak clasped with a gold brooch with an image of a dog preying on a fawn. This cloak and brooch were given to Odysseus by Penelope when he left for Troy. This image of a dog could be a remnant of the original myth before *The Iliad* connection created by Homer.

THE LOCATION OF THE ROYAL THOLOS

When viewed from Kangelisses Kokolata, Kefalonia, with its unique encircling horizon, the surrounding landscape offers a visually impressive "framing" for the constellations and specific sun and moon rises. The locals were aware of this long ago.

Odysseus was well aware of the unique horizon encircling sacred Kangelisses. He also felt his accomplishments in life would not be enough to be remembered for generations. This leader wanted something more permanent. He believed that being attached to solar and lunar holidays and future stories inspired by constellations in the sky would ensure immortality. The best location for a tomb, for someone seeking immortality in myth, was to be seen next to these immortal constellations.

He knew the universal cosmic story of the hunter and prey and how they became constellations. He also knew that he and the new elite, a mixing of northerners and natives, would always need to be associated with the sun and moon, even in death, for successive generations to maintain legitimacy in rule. The older, early Greek heroes such as Perseus and Hercules, probably early Proto-Greek Indo-European heroes, and much older Orion (possible Egyptian roots, Old Kingdom, or even Neolithic), had already found their places in the constellations. He wanted something similar. He wanted to be remembered; he wanted his story to be retold forever.

The best that this Middle Helladic warlord could have done was to have his tomb built at a unique location on the horizon where the sun sets on the date of a festival and next to the immortal inhabitants (the constellations) of the wine-dark sea (the starry night sky.) Thus, his adventures and stories would be told during winter solstice rituals, along with the stories of early Greek heroes.

Every year, worshippers would celebrate Odysseus' return to "Ithaca." Located at that point on the horizon, he would become an active participant in the constellations and forever be connected to the sun and moon. And so, the sun sets on the royal tholos - every twelve months – the number that identifies him and Ithaca in *The Odyssey*. After the completion of nineteen years, a unique new moon coincides with the winter solstice on the first day of the twentieth year. Furthermore, we have a lunar standstill observable from Archangelo, where the moon sets near the peak of Lakithra almost every two decades. These astronomical events cannot be coincidental. These events were worshipped at Kokolata-Livatho and gave rise to the myth of Odysseus, which ultimately became an epic.

About 750 years later, Homer learned of this local story retold by countless bards, created his *Odyssey*, and tied it to *The Iliad*.

The one characteristic that separated Odysseus from all other heroes of Greek lore was his intelligence. The selection of his final resting place was brilliant.

NOTES/CONCLUSIONS:

The images are an artist's work - the ancients may have seen the constellations somewhat differently. There were fewer constellations in 1600 BC than there are today.

I chose to focus on the older constellations mentioned in *The Odyssey*. I also chose the months November - December, when the last part of *The Odyssey* likely takes place, before the winter solstice - The Return of Odysseus and the Feast of Apollo. Many have concluded that Odysseus killed the suitors during the winter solstice. The winter solstice at the end of the Middle Helladic period occurred at the beginning of January. Therefore, I see the story in the constellations lasting two months before the winter solstice. Note: a partial solar eclipse occurred only ten days after the winter solstice of 1601 BC. This eclipse will be discussed in the following chapter.

My conclusion is the cemetery of Kangelisses, and the royal tholos at Lakithra would have been constructed during this period. They were the founders of a new society and a new era. Moreover, Kangelisses was most likely already considered a sacred area – Early Bronze Age pottery sherds were found in the area during a field survey. (Souyoudzoglou-Haywood 2008.)

A BRIEF HISTORY OF THE CONSTELLATIONS
IN ANCIENT GREECE

The history of today's constellations, including the observations of Claudius Ptolemy in 150 BC, is very complex.

Modern astronomers have used various analyses to determine when and even where (analyzing views by latitude) the first known constellations were created. The earth's latitude plays a vital role because the farther south or north one goes, the less or more they see of the southern or northern constellations.

As an aside, the ancients that extensively traveled north to south were probably the first to notice that the earth may not have been flat. They noticed how for example, a southern constellation was much higher above the horizon the further south they went. This phenomenon is due to the earth's curvature, so an ancient person in Upper Egypt, for example, would see the celestial sphere differently than he would see them while traveling the Black Sea.

In ancient times, the observation of constellations served various purposes: 1) Inspiration for myths, 2) for use as forecasts for agricultural purposes or specific hunting seasons, and 3) for navigational purposes.

My conclusion is that most of the constellations used by the early Greeks (Mycenaeans and after) have their roots in the initial Minoan thalassocracy. But it is also likely that the Indo-European Proto-Greeks had brought with them their constellation-inspired myths.

The Minoan knowledge of constellations was also likely heavily influenced by the astronomy of Babylon and Egypt.

It was a long process of evolution, from the Paleolithic era to the Iron Age, as we see in the works of Hesiod and Homer.

For an interesting celestial analysis of Minoan seals and the "floating objects" depicted on them, see Kyriakidis, 2005. In his research, he concludes that these objects represented Minoan constellations.

6

THE ECLIPSE OF 1601 BC

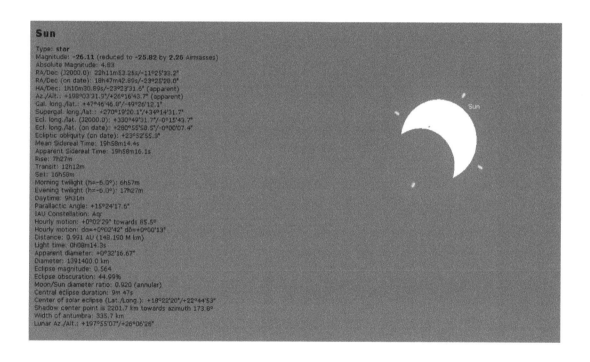

Fig. 46. Stellarium sky view from Kangelisses,
partial eclipse, 44.99% coverage, 1601 BC

Eleven days after the winter solstice on Jan. 14, 1601 BC, while the sun was still setting in the area of the royal tholos, there was a partial solar eclipse.

Fig. 47. Stellarium sky/topography photo of Lakithra Peak,
1601 BC, almost three hours later.

As the sun approached the royal tholos, the sun outran the moon, and the solar eclipse ended.

For the ancients, this would have been important for two likely reasons. First, had the tomb been already built - it would have been viewed as a miracle worthy of a myth. Or, if the legend had already existed, another story would have been added to it explaining a challenge Odysseus, the solar hero, overcame to return to Ithaca. Second, if the tomb did not exist at the location, it gave rise to one being built there.

Such celestial phenomena inspired myth creation. Myths are a long process, an evolution. As successive generations retold the myth, local mythology evolved, and parts of the story changed.

Could the name Calypso and this eclipse be related? Odysseus left Calypso in his twentieth year, and the words Calypso and eclipse share the same root word, "to cover."

The days of the solstices and equinox mark seasons. However, the dates are not fixed due to the earth's precession – the gradual change in the tilt of the earth's axis. In 1601 BC, using the current calendar in Stellarium, the winter solstice would be on January 3 and not on December 21 as it is today.

There is more that can also be interpreted from this event, though it is important to know that it must have been a clear day for all these celestial observances. January in Kefalonia is part of the rainy season, and cloud cover is typical.

Both Venus and Mercury/Hermes rose that day, just before dawn. Hermes relayed the message from Zeus to Calypso that Odysseus be freed to go back home. (*Odyssey* 5.95-115)

A few hours earlier during the night, the constellations mentioned in Book 5, lines 270-275, which include the directions Calypso gave Odysseus for his return home, take important positions relative to the cist graves at Kangelisses:

> "Gladly then did goodly Odysseus spread his sail to the breeze; and he sat and guided his raft skillfully with the steering-oar, nor did sleep fall upon his eyelids, as he watched the ***Pleiads,*** and late-setting ***Bootes***, and the ***Bear***, which men also call the Wain, whichever circles where it is and watches ***Orion***, and alone has no part in the baths of Ocean. For this star Calypso, the beautiful goddess, had bidden him to keep on the left hand as he sailed over the sea." (Homer, *Odyssey*, Transl. A.T. Murray, 1919)

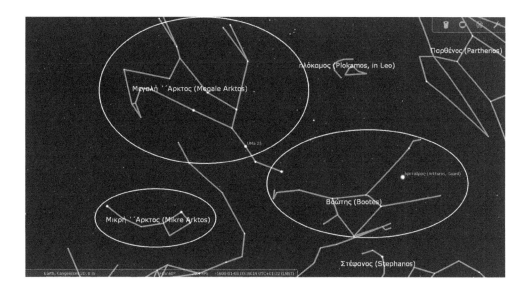

Fig. 48. Stellarium sky over Kangelisses, 1601 BC. The Almagest constellations are visible over the two pairs of cist graves north of the central cist grave.

Interestingly, all the above constellations in fig. 48 lie above and parallel to the two pairs of graves. Due to the trees, it was not possible to photograph the ground against the sky/horizon, so I will describe what I saw in my simulation. The constellation Bootes (right, fig. 48) lies horizontally above cist graves 3-4; these are the two cists that mark the summer solstice sunrise (cist 3) and the heliacal rise of the star Arcturus (cist 4). Meanwhile, the bears, the Great Bear (Megale Arktos), also called the wagon in the past, as well as the Little Bear (Mikre Arktos), are above cist graves 5-6.

If at that exact moment we turn around and look directly opposite the constellations over the cist graves, behind us facing southwest, we see the following exhibited in Fig. 49.

The rest of the constellations Calypso mentions are evident: Orion and also the Pleiades as part of the constellation Taurus. The date in both images above is the night before the winter solstice. It seems to me to have been a perfect alignment of constellations with the cist graves at Kangelisses and the royal tholos at Lakithra, all visible from Kangelisses. It's as if someone saw these alignments at the same time. These specific alignments could have been seen any year during the Middle Helladic and even into the Late Helladic.

Following page: Fig. 49. 1601 BC Stellarium sky simulation and landscape photo from Kangelisses, 1601 BC. The Almagest constellations over the royal tholos: Argo, Kyon (the dog), Orion, and Taurus with the Pleiades.

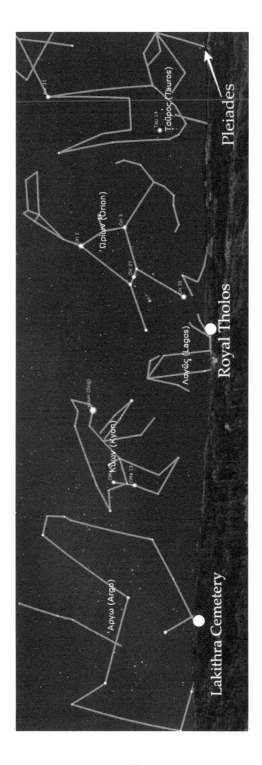

Perhaps the Calypso episode in *The Odyssey* was inspired by this moment in time when the locals were viewing the constellations from the Kangelisses cemetery. They noticed how the constellations' positions were unique to the graves at Kangelisses, a sacred cemetery, and the royal tholos on the horizon. Orion and the Pleiades (part of Taurus) pass just above the royal tholos and set.

With modern technology, we can now observe the exact day or night sky that the ancients observed from their sacred locations. This is an excellent use of technology that researchers should use more often. Quite the opposite has occurred for long enough. We have dismissed a vital part of the ancients' life, the sky and the constellations they followed. These observances were part of their daily lives for navigating the seas, for agricultural planning, and just as important, for inspiration in creating the myths of their heroes. Observing the ancient sky gives us a better understanding of prehistoric people.

7

SPATIAL AND CELESTIAL RELATIONS OF BRONZE AGE SITES IN THE KOKOLATA/ LIVATHO AREA

When we look at the major Bronze Age sites in Kokolata-Livatho, and their spatial relationships to each other, we see that their locations were carefully selected to align with each other. These spatial relationships were based on a celestial body or a common distance. Similar conclusions have been reached by Blomberg and Henricksson (2014, p. 1433) about the alignments of individual buildings in Minoan Crete: "Orientations were usually marked by a natural or an artificial foresight, i.e., a prominent natural feature such as a mountain peak or a manmade construction such as a column. This indicates that the alignment of buildings to the celestial bodies was of vital importance in Minoan cosmology, *connecting their world to the celestial sphere*." (emphasis mine – KNK)

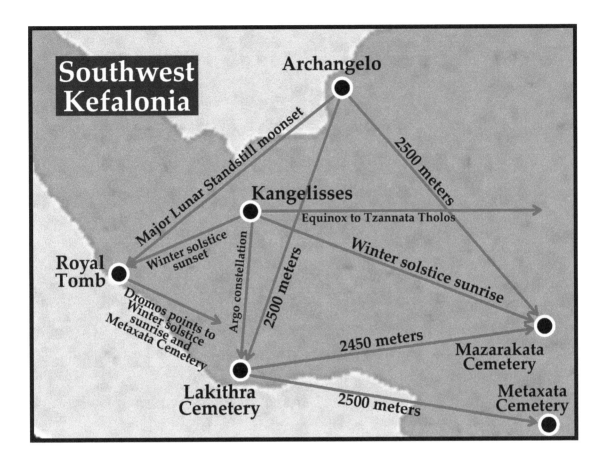

Fig. 50. Sites in Kokolata-Livatho, unique spatial relationships
(the dark grey area represents heightened elevation)

Likely chronological order of construction:

1) Archangelo Cult Center (MHII - circa 1900 BC)

2) Kangelisses cemetery and royal tomb (MHIII - circa 1600/1550 BC)

3) Unidentified structure at Archangelo (the latest LHIIIA2, circa 1390, probably well before)

4) Lakithra, Mazarakata, and Metaxata cemeteries (LHIIIA2 - circa 1390 BC)

I believe the Bronze Age inhabitants of Kokolata-Livatho felt a sense of inferiority being a smaller community compared to the larger evolving centers on Crete and the Peloponnesian mainland. They compensated for this by taking a grander approach, by pleasing the solar deity not with individual impressive buildings or cemeteries but with the alignments of all their sacred sites of worship, which, taken as a whole, represent a grand, comprehensive approach to land planning. As the solar deity rose from beneath the earth and viewed this well-planned civilization, the deity would be impressed by how this small area of the world aligned all their sacred sites. They would look down kindly on them. In addition, each site that aligned with other sites would "share" their sacred significance.

HOW IT ALL BEGAN

In 2019, after observing some ancient remains in Kokolata (which turned out to be of the Hellenistic period), I began researching the Bronze Age in Kefalonia. After looking at several maps of Bronze Age sites from published papers, I noticed some distances between places seemed equal. I would use Google Earth to identify ancient sites and measure the distances between them. Initially, I believed that an equilateral triangle would have been formed using the Mazarakata and Lakithra cemeteries, two prominent Late Helladic cemeteries. I searched the area where the apex of the equilateral triangle would be and found nothing.

I headed back to that location in the summer of 2020, thinking maybe it would be an isosceles triangle, and by chance, that apex would be further north, in family property. Walking about 50 meters into the family property, I noticed a deep recess carved into the property's hillside. It turns out to be a buried structure, with somewhat of an apse carved into the stone hillside, and extends for about 30 meters. I checked the distance on Google Maps, and there it was – an isosceles triangle. It looks like an apsidal structure possibly turned into a heroon. I say it could be a heroon (hero worship structure that may have had a different prior use) because of its equidistant relation to the cemeteries and a concave carving on the exposed boulders, similar to what I had seen at the solar cult center. Moreover, there seems to be a circular pedestal next to the "apse" area for an important person – possibly added to the structure much later for ceremonies.

I continued walking the property and found many remains such as walls, randomly located Hellenistic/Roman and possibly older era looted graves, and a large stone entrance connecting two levels of the property. As I was exploring, a dog was about to attack me at one point, and as I stood my ground, I heard a voice calling for his dog. It was an acquaintance that used two of our family properties for his goats to graze.

I told him that I saw many unusual stone structures on the property that seemed ancient. He said yes, and told me to follow him up a very wooded terraced hillside full of giant boulders, some minimally carved. He showed me what ultimately turned out to be the Archangelo cult center. It was covered under trees and thick brush, but there were visible signs that this was no ordinary geological phenomenon. People carved the boulders in the deep past. The nearby randomly located Hellenistic graves carved into the exposed bedrock and possible libation depressions near these "less ancient" graves gave me the impression this general area was a much older sacred site that the later ancients used as a cemetery. They must have known that an older civilization existed there, that it was something of significance, possibly to do with "the era of heroes." Just over 300 meters away, a Hellenistic/Roman period cemetery looted long ago seemed to have been very organized. At Archangelo, similar graves (rectangularly carved pits into the exposed bedrock) are very random. One such grave, for example, is next to a road, with multiple parallel wheel ruts, chariot, and wagon widths, that seems to begin from the area of the cult center and continues under a sizeable defensive wall and beyond.

It is interesting to note that years before, I had walked parts of that property and noticed a large, long stone pile I stood on to get a better view of the second lower level. Years later, I realized that was no stone pile. Farmers did not build it to delineate a boundary or create a terrace for agricultural purposes. The outer walls were carefully chosen flat-faced stones with shapes that "locked" with each other with rubble in the middle. It was a long, wide, incomplete defensive wall that collapsed long ago.

I am still researching the equidistant relationships that additional sites share with others.

8

SUMMARY AND CONCLUSIONS

THE HOMERIC EPICS DO NOT TELL THE STORY OF A SINGULAR ERA

Homeric realists that take much of *The Odyssey* as accurate and construct theories based on a few phrases regarding the topography or geography of "Ithaca" overlook the deep history of *The Odyssey* and the symbolic references to astronomy, which in the Neolithic and early Bronze Age, were a large part of religion. Astronomy back then was not the study of celestial bodies as we know of today but the observation of divinities (heavenly bodies such as the sun) that were highly predictable. That predictability must have been a source of comfort to the ancients. Unexplainable events outside of that predictability, such as a comet or a lunar or solar eclipse, was an irregularity that needed interpretation. Furthermore, as civilizations arose based on surplus food from improved agricultural practices, the calendar played a vital role in agricultural planning.

Most people agree that the epics are not a sequential series of historical events. I further submit that we should not date *The Iliad* and *The Odyssey* to the 13th century BC. These two epics are a mixture of events that began with the early Greek migration and conquest/assimilation and ended with the collapse of the Bronze Age – events that were last synthesized and edited by a brilliant and talented bard in the Iron Age. By the time Homer finished his version of *The Odyssey*, many centuries had passed since the Bronze Age, and the Greek religion evolved significantly from what people worshipped in the Middle Helladic period.

The religion practiced by the Greeks when they initially settled in Greece was not the same. We see in *The Odyssey* the pantheon of gods that we know of today. Some of the gods were worshipped, judging by certain Linear-B tablets, but when we look at Mycenaean art, we still see many Minoan motifs that represent a female solar deity and her partner or son. Did they also initially worship the same gods the natives who migrated earlier from Anatolia worshipped? Or did wealthy Mycenaeans hire Minoan artists to create objects such as seal rings that they considered merely exotic items for the new aristocracy? Most likely, there was an assimilation of cultures that, in the long run, ultimately became the more warrior-like, more masculine sky-god-centered ancient Greek religion we know of today.

I agree with a conclusion reached by Adam Nicolson in *The Mighty Dead: Why Homer Matters* (2014). If Greek mythology is Mycenaean mythology, it would have its roots in the deep Mycenaean past and influenced by Minoan/Aegean practices. The culture of the peak palatial period (1400-1200 BC) was too mature/ bureaucratic in development to create new myths or to live as the heroes in the myths had lived. It is more likely that the Late Helladic rulers sought symbolic ties with the older Middle Helladic and beyond heroes to gain legitimacy. These heroes were the founders of a new world that assimilated two cultures and religions.

The 15th century BC Griffin Warrior's grave at Pylos is an example of this assimilation. Countless Minoan or Minoan-inspired artifacts were found at the grave of a Mycenaean leader, including the famous Pylos combat agate. Sharon Stocker, the lead archaeologist at the Griffin Warrior grave, states this plainly: "The Griffin Warrior is saying, 'I'm part of that Minoan world." (Curry, 2019). Ultimately, Stocker was proven correct. In a recently published article, Lazaridis et al. (2022) found that the Griffin Warrior had no detectable Eastern European hunter-gatherer ancestry. He was either a native to the region or an individual with Cretan roots, if not directly from Crete. So here we see that by the Late Bronze Age (c.1450), the assimilation between Greek-speaking Indo-Europeans and natives with Neolithic Anatolian roots was complete. Ancestry was not a factor in either ruling elites or ordinary people. Interestingly, this individual was buried in a shaft grave, a burial style associated with mainland Mycenaeans and not Minoan Crete.

Therefore, as I have mentioned, there was cultural assimilation between these two groups. Nonetheless, for some reason still unknown, Greek did become the dominant language. Furthermore, by the Iron Age, as we see in the works of Homer and Hesiod, the dominant religion had Indo-European roots. Zeus was the primary deity, a sky-father type god. What happened to the solar goddess? A religious reformation of sorts must have occurred over time.

In the combat agate from the Griffin Warrior's grave and similar seals from Mycenae, we see the motif of mortal combat. Could these war scenes be indicative of a Greek mainland collective myth of warriors that eventually inspired *The Iliad*? (See: Lewartowski, Kazimierz, 2019) Could the signet rings depicting the meeting of the divine couple, with solar and lunar motifs, have inspired *The Odyssey* and the actual theocratic system of government on Kefalonia – that is, a royal couple that represented those two deities? If this is true for both scenarios, then the war in *The Iliad* is not a historical account of the 13th century, nor is its "spin-off" *The Odyssey*. The Homeric epics have much deeper roots.

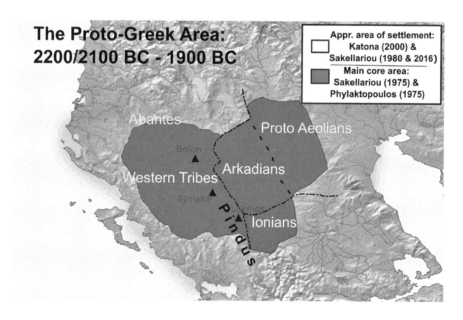

Fig. 51. Proto Greek Area 2200/2100 - 1900 BC
Source: Wikimedia Commons, Alexikoua

By 1900 BC, Greek speakers began entering Greece. Amongst the Western Tribes: The Kephallenian Tribe mentioned by Homer. Had these Greek speakers reached Kefalonia (not on the map) by the 1600s BC?

The Middle Helladic period in Greece marks the end of the early Greek speaker migration that initially began in the steppes of Eastern Europe to where Greece is today. This period is when these new migrants either founded new centers or, more likely, some gained entry into the existing elite. The Middle Helladic is the possible period where pieces of historical facts of the era evolved into myths about city founders and heroic deeds. A "reformation" of the local religion would also have gradually occurred, culminating in the religion described centuries later by Homer and Hesiod. I believe the common goal of Hesiod and Homer was to "standardize" religion and culture in the Greek world.

AN INDO-EUROPEAN EXAMPLE

The epics are full of astronomical allegories and stories with Indo-European roots that can be found even in distant North India (the Hindu epic: *The Mahabharata*).

The similar *Odyssey* and *Mahabharata* storyline involves an archery competition that requires stringing a bow and shooting an almost impossible target. The contestant is a disguised yet royal man who aims to marry a royal woman. These two scenes share many similarities and are rooted in an oral tradition going back millennia. Most likely, this was an ancient Indo-European wedding ritual for a woman from a wealthy family.

This archery contest could have been not only a story but an actual ritual between prominent families. Thus, in *The Odyssey*, we see an Indo-European story and practice brought by the migrating Greek speakers that likely made its way into the original Odysseus myth before Homer. It may as well have been an actual practice.

THE BRONZE AGE COLLAPSE

Even though Homer's *Iliad* describes a war between the Achaeans and Ilion (Troy/Wilusa), archaeological evidence is still inconclusive. Furthermore, many Mycenaean centers had collapsed in the same period or before the destruction of Troy/Wilusa in 1180/1190 BC.

It is implausible that Homer would have known the dates of each Mycenaean center's destruction. And so, many surviving Achaean leaders had no home to return to and no citadel to rule after the sack of Troy. Yet, in *The Odyssey*, Homer has Nestor safely back in Pylos and Menelaus in Sparta.

Various factors had likely caused the Bronze Age collapse. (See: Cline, 2014) Cline and others have mentioned, among other factors, an earthquake swarm and famine due to a prolonged drought. There was also a "federation" of people from various parts of the Mediterranean called the "Sea People," a term created by French Egyptologist Emmanuel de Rougé. The Sea People were not just a marauding army but a massive migration of people, displaced for some unknown reason, searching to conquer lands for their families. They brought their families and possessions – they were not some professional army sent by a ruler. For some reason, they could no longer live in their original lands. They formed large armadas that raided coastal cities, hence the name "Sea People."

Many researchers believe that the Greeks were part of the Sea People who invaded Egypt. Most likely, the Sea People, with their impressive armadas mentioned by Ramses III, were the historical memory that inspired Homer's *Iliad*, or at least the launching of a "thousand ships." There were two waves of attacks on Egypt from these Sea People. The first was in 1207 BC, during the reign of Merneptah, and the second was in 1174 BC, during the reign of Ramses III.

Thus, the two most globally significant wars of that era were in Egypt involving the Sea People. There is a blurring of history here. The Iron Age Homeric epics seem to borrow and dig much deeper into history. For example, the use of Indo-European motifs and Middle Helladic Greek heroes/ founders. The epics also blur the events of the later Bronze Age collapse, hence the "tragic victory" of the epic cycle, more tragic than victorious, which would be much closer to the historical truth.

Under such instability, which would have led the commoners to question the legitimacy of the ruling elite and political system, did the local populations rebel against the ruling caste? It is important to note that such a collapse did not occur in Kefalonia; Kefalonia continued to thrive (Metaxas, 2022). But regardless of what happened in the

Greek world, the collapse occurred throughout the eastern Mediterranean. Only Egypt survived to a degree and was never as strong after that.

I mention the Bronze Age collapse because it is highly unusual for such a historical event to have been ignored by Homer. If Homer's tale of Troy is accurate, rulers such as Menelaus and Nestor would have returned home to destroyed citadels. Moreover, Telemachus' journey to the Peloponnese in search of news about his father would have been very different. Telemachus would have seen one citadel after the other destroyed by fire. Yet Homeric realists still accept many details of *The Odyssey*, such as the geography of Ithaca.

Moreover, *The Odyssey* is far from a lesson in central Ionian geography. From the times of Eratosthenes and Strabo, people have debated which islands are located in which areas, which bay or other topographic feature was mentioned in *The Odyssey*, etc. A poet will sacrifice such insignificant narrative facts for poetic license in favor of the allegories and didactic elements that were always essential.

AN ADDITIONAL CAUSE
OF THE BRONZE AGE COLLAPSE

Various factors have been attributed to the Bronze Age collapse of the Eastern Mediterranean, but I believe one factor seems to have been either overlooked or not given enough attention. If government and religion were intertwined and ruling elites were connected to the sun and other deities to establish legitimacy, natural factors such as earthquake storms and famine brought by drought would have been seen as challenges to the authority of the elite and the religion they espoused. If periods of prosperity strengthened the legitimacy of the elites' rule, the opposite also holds. That is, periods of natural disasters were looked upon as events the elites were incapable of controlling, and thus their religion would also have been held accountable.

Before the Bronze Age collapse in Greece, there must have been a secondary religion, brought by the Greek Speaking Indo-Europeans, that had many adherents during the Bronze Age. Aspects of this religion must have survived the assimilation between the

Greek speakers and natives. Of course, judging by Late Helladic glyptic art, it seems the elites may have continued worshipping the female solar deity. By the Iron Age, however, all remnants of the female solar deity were gone – Zeus, the sky father, was supreme.

If we go back in time to the Thera (Santorini) eruption approximately 350 years before, we see another natural event that must have destabilized society. The Thera eruption dates sometime between the end of the Middle Helladic period and the beginning of the Late Helladic period, the era of assimilation between Indo-European Greek speakers and natives. The natural disaster caused by the Thera eruption must have influenced the religion of many societies, and some Greek speakers must have used it to their advantage in elevating their status and religion.

Overall, I believe the evolution of religion was a gradual process, which slowly grew until it exploded as a significant religious movement during the Bronze Age collapse. During the instability caused by famines and earthquakes, the legitimacy of institutions was questioned, and citadels were ultimately burned down. To attack the elites was also to attack the religious status quo. Post Bronze Age, the religions followed by most in the eastern Mediterranean changed dramatically, except for Egypt.

THE KEPHALLENE EXPLORERS

The Odyssey is also a story of adventure based on the experiences of Greek explorers of the west. Which area in the central Ionian had the population and the source of timber for ships (fir trees of the species Abies Cephalonica from Mount Ainos) to be built and have enough rowers for a small navy plus a deep, calm harbor for its ships to explore west of the Aegean? It is only the Kokolata-Livatho region. Over time, many of the exaggerated sailors' stories about the wild west, outside the known Aegean world, became myths, ultimately incorporated into one man's experiences.

Judging by the archaeological record and numerous field surveys for pottery sherds, the Kokolata-Livatho region had the largest population and tomb evidence of travel in all the central Ionian. However, even if Kokolata-Livatho did not have a fleet for long voyages, it likely had more available rowers/warriors traveling on Peloponnesian or Cretan ships - a collaboration of sorts. The populations of the neighboring areas, including Ithaca, were not large enough to contribute many if any, sailors for such expeditions. They needed healthy men to defend their homes from pirate attacks.

Apart from Kokolata-Livatho, no other area in the central Ionian could lose men to "sea adventures" - the protection of the homeland was more critical. Of all the cemeteries in the area, the Lakithra cemetery had items that could be associated with warriors who had traveled abroad (Weapons and Italian items). Ithaca, by contrast, has meager evidence despite two centuries of ongoing archaeological excavations.

I believe *The Iliad* was much more a literary construct than a historical record of a Late Bronze Age event. Judging by the mortal combat seal rings discussed earlier, there may have already been material for Homer to use in creating his *Iliad.* Furthermore, he likely connected an existing myth of an Ionian Sea warlord based in Kefalonia to *The Iliad*.

In *Rise of the Greek Epic,* Gilbert Murray, in describing the Odysseus character's involvement in *The Iliad,* concludes as follows:

> "Odysseus, though now prominent in the *Iliad*, seems as a saga figure to have had little or nothing to do with Troy. In the Odyssey he is mostly a folk-lore hero with folk-lore adventures, though, of course, one can never be sure that these adventures have not been attached to a historic name." (1924, p. 210)

Odysseus' story was about an adventure into the wild and newly explored west - an environment very different from the advanced civilized east. Various adventures and exaggerated stories that had been told for a long time by many explorers telescoped into one person's life story.

Myths, over time, often attain a level of grandeur that does not resemble the original story. For our traveling warrior/warlord, during his absence, his estate was slowly confiscated by the neighboring villagers – something that happens even today when a family leaves a village in Kefalonia. (I know from personal experience managing family properties and coming up against pastoral "squatters.") As the story grew and spread to other areas, it gained a level of grandeur that included a king of a much larger region, albeit with many geographical errors.

For example, the Noah and the Flood myth similarly had simpler roots. Here, we see a basic story of a family's experience of extreme flooding, possibly along the Tigris or Euphrates, that ultimately turned into a global flood retold over millennia. The story began with a farmer safeguarding his family and livestock on a boat which later became an ark with two of every animal in the known world. (The reality: the farmer only needed two of each domesticated animal to save space on his small boat and restart his farm after the flood.) The eventual resting place of Noah's Ark, specifically on Mt. Ararat in modern Turkey, is an example of a myth's geography run amok over centuries of retelling.

Was Odysseus missing from Ithaca for twenty years? Hardly. As discussed before, the two decades were a lunar allegory for either the Metonic cycle or the lunar standstill. But, we can easily imagine a seafaring warrior not returning to his homeland when expected due to circumstances beyond his control.

Very likely, the situation on his estate would have degraded in his absence. Thus, the end of *The Odyssey*: The warrior's return was violent, but the local customs and social mores were re-imposed. Stability and order followed. The warrior's revenge served as a warning to those who wanted to take advantage of a seafarer's estate during his absence. It was a didactic story told with the goal of preserving and protecting a local budding maritime tradition. Parallel to that, it was also a solar metaphor of Odysseus as the sun returning to that peak.

SCIENCE, RELIGION, AND GOVERNANCE
WERE ONE BODY OF KNOWLEDGE

The Bronze Age ancients, beginning with Sumer, were intrigued by the measurable, predictable clockwork of the heavenly bodies they observed. This knowledge spread to Babylonia, Egypt, Crete, and beyond. Celestial and calendrical allegories have always been part of the story - inspired by the "journeys" of the sun, moon, and constellations over the royal tomb. Thus, in the myth of *Odysseus*, we also find an astronomy and calendar lesson for the few who understood it and used it for religious purposes to bond a community.

Whereas *The Iliad* begins with an angered Apollo, *The Odyssey* begins with an angered Helios. Helios was the clue for those in the ancient audience that had astronomical (which is to say, religious) knowledge of what was to follow parallel to the story. It was an utter brilliance in story design.

Centuries later, classical commentators stated certain aspects of epics should not be changed by storytellers. They likely referred to the scientific astronomic observations embedded in the stories. Literary license was allowed, so long as the parallel lesson, explained through allegories, in science/religion was unaltered. (regarding allegorical exegesis, see: Grey, 2018).

The sun was central to religions from the Neolithic well into the Bronze Age. It gave vegetation life, emitted warmth, lit the environment, and if one stared at it for too long, it could permanently damage one's eyesight. What other observable god offered such tangible, provable results? One can understand Pharaoh Akhenaten's push for a monotheistic solar religion. It was the most logical to him; he saw the sun as a universal phenomenon, and all civilizations relied on it for survival.

Yet *The Odyssey* contains many other parallel themes and thus remains many things to many people, as all such great works of literature do. The myth of Odysseus, to the well-educated Bronze Age audience, and later, Homer's *Odyssey*, to the well-educated Iron Age audience, was always considered a repository of knowledge woven into a story. I will even go as far as saying the creation of the Antikythera mechanism was inspired by the celestial and calendrical allegories found in *The Odyssey*.

A REVIEW OF THE SIMILARITIES BETWEEN THE ODYSSEY AND THE KOKOLATA-LIVATHO REGION

A man and his dog meet again - The constellation Canis Major/Kyon, the dog, in early November, fades/dies as it approaches the royal tholos. This celestial event is also the star Sirius' cosmic setting. The constellation next to the dog is the "Argo," Jason's ship. Coincidently, it is also the name of Odysseus' dog. In *The Odyssey*, Argo dies when he finally sees his owner again. As alluded to earlier, death and dogs have deep Neolithic and

Indo-European roots. Furthermore, this event, described in *The Odyssey* as the meeting of dog and master but actually was the cosmic setting of the star Sirius, was likely a special day on their calendar. It marked two months before their winter solstice holiday.

The constellations Taurus and Orion pass over the tomb. Here again, we see a piece of The Odyssey when Eurycleia identifies Odysseus by a scar caused by a boar's tusk while hunting. Orion is seen dangerously close to the constellation Taurus' horns. Thus, this constellation and the Canis Major/Kyon constellation identify Odysseus both in the story and over the tomb.

Solar metaphors abound in the Odyssey – In Bronze Age Kokolata-Livatho, we see a culture that worshipped the sun and located cemeteries and tombs along solstice alignments. The solar cult center at Archangelo and the solar design of the cemetery at Kangelisses are examples. *The Odyssey* begins with an angered Helios, the sun god.

The crew of Odysseus - The Lakithra cemetery with views of both Mt. Ainos and the sea, of seafaring warriors, with males injured by hand-to-hand combat, and rich deposits of foreign objects and weapons is symbolic of the crew of Odysseus. The constellation Argo passes above this cemetery and continues to set on the horizon at the royal tholos.

Odysseus was missing for two decades; he commanded twelve ships, he shot an arrow through twelve axes, and Ithaca had twelve suitors and maidens. From allegory to reality: a royal tholos where the sun sets every twelve months and a full and new moon return after the completion of nineteen years. Furthermore, from the Archangelo cult center, the major lunar standstill reaches the area of the tholos almost every two decades. I consider these solar and lunar phenomena the most critical elements that connect the creation of *The Odyssey* with the location of Kokolata-Livatho. We must not forget that these celestial phenomena were witnessed and celebrated by a hero cult. Hero cults are the precursors to myths of heroic individuals; ultimately, this particular myth became an epic. Finally, we also have "nostos," the return of Odysseus in the myth, and the return of the sun to the tomb of Odysseus. Douglas Frame analyzed the root "nes," which he shows a connection to "nostos," which itself has an underlying meaning of "return to light."

(Frame, 1978) The return of the winter solstice sun to the royal tomb of Lakithra fits this analysis and is beyond coincidence. It is interesting to note that Frame mentions in his commentary of "nostos" the following: "Such is the scanty—but significant—evidence provided by Greek sun worship, which for the most part was quicker to die than the epic tradition."

Odysseus as the sun, leaving Calypso and returning home (the tholos) an eclipse and a woman named Calypso - the sun outpaces the moon and sets/returns to the location of the royal tholos. The royal tholos was likely built around the same time as that particular eclipse. The Bronze Age ancients must have known that eclipses occur only during a new moon. They understood the connection between the sun and the moon during an eclipse.

Odysseus: a name with the root "Dys/Δυς," which means west and setting of the sun - the leader of this region performed ceremonies with the sun setting west behind him, as seen at Archangelo. His tomb is located at the sunset of a holy day – the winter solstice. He was the leader of the westernmost Greek center, which thus represented the "edge" of the Greek world: where the sun set last. Maybe it was always a "descriptive" title for the lord of the area, used by many for an extended period. This connection needs further research.

Motifs in Minoan signet rings resemble allegories and characters in The Odyssey and match the royal tholos' relationship to the sun and the moon. With the discovery of the combat agate at Pylos and its similarity to other seals of the same genre at other Mycenaean centers, more researchers and academics are seeing a connection between these combat seal rings in Mycenaean centers and the warrior stories in *The Iliad*.

We can now say another relationship exists between a Homeric epic and signet rings. In *The Odyssey*, we have the reunion of Penelope and Odysseus at the new moon at the winter solstice, which also occurs over the royal tholos tomb. We see signet rings depicting a divine couple/sacred conversation related to the sun and sometimes the moon. These are signs of much older, pre-Homeric, myths of the Greek world. Homer simply connected the two into related epics.

THE ODYSSEY AS A CALENDAR

The archaeological record regarding calendar use in Bronze Age Greece is not as rich as in the Near East. Since knowledge spread from the earliest Mesopotamian civilizations of Sumer/ Babylonia east to Anatolia, Egypt, Crete, and mainland Greece, we should look to Mesopotamia and Egypt for clues.

Two calendars were used in Mesopotamia, beginning about 2600 BC and ending at 1000 BC. One calendar was a cultic calendar for dating, for example, holidays, and the other was an administrative one used for measuring time but not for dating. (Brack-Bernsen 2007 p. 155) In *The Odyssey*, the cultic calendar is described by the use of allegories.

Some more information is needed before we can see how Homer describes this cultic calendar. The cultic calendar was defined by the solar year and twelve lunar cycles. A lunar cycle, the moon's journey around the earth, lasts 29.5 days. That is to say, the time between one new moon and the next is 29.5 days. The same holds for one full moon to the next. These repetitive phases occur because as the moon travels around the earth, the amount of sunlight we see reflected on the moon changes.

However, counting a month as 29.5 days is awkward, so a system of alternating 29 and 30-day months was used. A 30-day month was a "full month," and a 29-day month was a "hollow" month. Hollow months were not considered to be as good as full months, and later on, we'll see how Doulichion was viewed in *The Odyssey* using a description of the hollow month.

Now the question of seasons must be addressed. The hidden calendar in *The Odyssey* used three seasons which would make sense because the weather was more variable in the Ionian Sea than in Mesopotamia. In Mesopotamia, given the warmer stable weather, two seasons were counted. In Egypt, however, due to flooding of the Nile, planting and harvesting times, three seasons were used in their calendar.

Therefore, if there are three seasons, each season has four months of alternating 29-day and 30-day months. Thus four months in a season: 2x30 + 2x29 = 118 days.

However, twelve lunar months of alternating 29/30 days are less than the solar year - the remaining days may have been added at the end of the year as a public holiday. For example, the festival of Apollo at the end of *The Odyssey* could have been a long holiday. In Mesopotamia, the remaining days were added every few years as an extra month.

The 118-day season is allegorically described (three times) in *The Odyssey*. The summary below is from Florence and Kenneth Wood's *Homer's Secret Odyssey* (2011).

If we count the number of people that Telemachus mentions to Odysseus who would be in the hall (108 suitors and ten others), the total is 118. Was it possible for that many people to be in a Bronze Age megaron/hall in the Ionian? Hardly - the number is an allegory. Furthermore, Odysseus is assisted by three individuals: Telemachus, Eumaios, and Philoetius. I believe these three individuals also represent the three seasons. The relevant passage lists the individuals as follows:

ἐκ μὲν Δουλιχίοιο δύω καὶ πεντήκοντα
κοῦροι κεκριμένοι, ἓξ δὲ δρηστῆρες ἕπονται·
ἐκ δὲ Σάμης πίσυρές τε καὶ εἴκοσι φῶτες ἔασιν,
ἐκ δὲ Ζακύνθου ἔασιν ἐείκοσι κοῦροι Ἀχαιῶν,
ἐκ δ᾽ αὐτῆς Ἰθάκης δυοκαίδεκα πάντες ἄριστοι,
καί σφιν ἅμ᾽ ἐστὶ Μέδων κῆρυξ καὶ θεῖος ἀοιδὸς
καὶ δοιὼ θεράποντε, δαήμονε δαιτροσυνάων.

"From Dulichium there are **two and fifty** chosen youths, and **six** serving men attend them; from Same came **four and twenty** men; from Zacynthus there are **twenty** youths of the Achaeans; and from Ithaca itself, **twelve** men, all of them the noblest, and with them is **Medon**, the herald, and the divine **minstrel**, and **two** squires skilled in carving meats."

(Homer Book 16 245-254 Trans. by A.T. Murray, 1919)

This number is repeated during the goat hunt. The number of goats that Odysseus and his crew captured can be computed as follows: 12 ships and 9 goats for each ship's crew, and 10 goats for Odysseus himself. (12x9) + 10 = 118. I would further add that the three bands/groups represent the three seasons.

αὐτίκα καμπύλα τόξα καὶ αἰγανέας δολιχαύλους
εἱλόμεθ᾽ ἐκ νηῶν, διὰ δὲ τρίχα κοσμηθέντες
βάλλομεν· αἶψα δ᾽ ἔδωκε θεὸς μενοεικέα θήρην.
νῆες μέν μοι ἕποντο δυώδεκα, ἐς δὲ ἑκάστην
ἐννέα λάγχανον αἶγες· ἐμοὶ δὲ δέκ᾽ ἔξελον οἴῳ.

Straightway we took from the ships our curved bows
and long javelins, and arrayed in **three bands** we fell to smiting;
and the god soon gave us game to satisfy our hearts. The
ships that followed me were **twelve, and to each nine**
goats fell by lot, but for me alone they chose out **ten.**

(Homer Book 9 156-160 Trans. by A.T. Murray, 1919)

Florence Wood also wrote of a final third season of 118 days that is allegorically described in *The Odyssey* at the end of the epic. It is Homer's description of Laertes' farm. After the killing of the suitors, Odysseus, Telemachus, Eumaios, and Philoetius flee to Laerte's farm. Odysseus has a conversation with his father, identifying himself by the old hunting scar and by an unusual numerical description of the farm.

Odysseus tells his father how, when he was young, he begged his father for the trees and vines on the farm. Odysseus repeated what Laertes gave him long ago: **13** pear trees, **10** apple trees, **40** fig trees, and **50** rows of vines. When Homer describes a numerical list, something may be behind it. Florence Wood concluded that the total comes to **113,** and if we add Odysseus, Laertes, Telemachus, Eumaios, and Philoetius, we arrive at 118. This allegory is the third and final **118**-day season in a lunar year.

There are many more such examples of allegories in *The Odyssey*. See Papathanassiou, 2008. Wood & Wood, 2011. Murray, 1924.

THE CALENDAR OF THE ODYSSEY ON A SEAL STONE
FROM KOKOLATA, KANGELISSES

I believe a seemingly abstract seal stone found in a Late Helladic grave at the Kangelisses cemetery represents a calendar (Fig. 52). This could have possibly been a replica of a larger object that functioned as a calendar. Pegs were likely used on the holes (triangles on seal stone) to track the days, months (lunar cycles), and seasons. The first column of three marks represents the three seasons in a year, as allegorically described in *The Odyssey*.

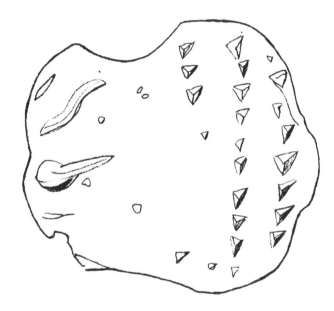

Fig. 52. Seal stone from Kangelisses Cemetery, Late Bronze Age

The second column that continues bottom left represents the twelve lunar months of the year. The third column is used in this manner: one starts counting the first small mark, counts down, and back up to the original mark to complete a half lunar cycle. Because a lunar month is approximately 29.5 days, the small top mark in the column is alternately counted twice or once as we count down and back up again. Admittedly, I am not sure about the remaining marks and what purpose they served. At the solar cult center, I mentioned the three large boulders/baetyls that lead up to the throne at the solar cult center. They, too, could have likely represented the three seasons.

Following along the lines of this 118-day season analysis, I found a source that provides a critique of such a theory. It is an article written for the journal *Classical Philology* by John A. Scott titled "Odysseus as a Sun God." For me, the value of this 1917 article was not the critique the author made but a specific quote from one named Altenburg that was approvingly used by one named Menrad. I have had difficulty finding the original works written in German. I used Google Translate to translate the referenced quote that was in German from Scott's article:

> "His wife, an earth goddess, was chosen by 118 suitors and their Companions. [He] urged, these are the 118 winter days, multiplied by 3, that form the lunar year. But the sun god Odysseus appears, admittedly weakened by winter, and therefore dressed as a beggar; he conquers the suitors and redeems the earth from winter. The master shot through the 12 axes signifies the sun god's victorious advance through the 12 months or the 12 images of the zodiac. The slain suitors are taken to Hades, i.e. the winter days disappear into the underworld." (Scott 1917, p. 244)

This quote above, quickly dismissed over a hundred years ago by the author John A. Scott, takes on a new meeting now that we know there is a royal tholos tomb where the sun sets every twelve months on the winter solstice. We also have a seal stone representing the same calendar found in *The Odyssey*. Moreover, this royal tholos is in Kefalonia; the same area generally agreed to be part of the Kingdom of Odysseus and the leader of the Kephallenes.

Hero worship took place at Kangelisses on the winter solstice. That is, the worshippers gathered at Kangelisses not only to see the winter solstice sunset but to see that unique sunset align with the burial tomb of their legendary hero. This hero worship and subsequent myth creation were products of the people of Kokolata Livatho and possibly the entire island's inhabitants. Much like the current holiday celebrating the island's patron saint,

Saint Gerasimos, when Kefalonians gather from every corner of the island, so too did the winter solstice at Kangelisses likely attracted the island's residents.

I can think of no other Bronze Age settlements in the Ionian with such a connection to *The Odyssey* and its hero, Odysseus. Many have analyzed the astronomical allegories of *The Odyssey;* this is not new. The finding of a royal tholos tomb located to show connections to the sun, moon, and constellations is new. It should now be considered when analyzing *The Odyssey* for its origins.

There is some historical authenticity in the epics, but not how most people currently believe, especially the Homeric realists. In *Odyssey* and the signet rings, we see hints of an older solar religion based on a divine couple, or maybe even a mother and warrior son – that became Penelope and Telemachus, whose name means "fighter from afar." Maybe in both Kefalonia and Minoan Crete, royal couples represented the divine couple. The royal tholos at Lakithra is the key. If it is not looted, or at least not severely looted, what will be found can change everything we know about *The Odyssey*.

WHAT THE DIFFERENT NUMBERS OF SUITORS MEAN

Homeric realists look to the number of suitors from each region as a reflection of the size or population of each island or area surrounding Odysseus' Ithaca. Since *The Odyssey* contains allegories of calendrical values, I believe it is best to continue with that analysis in trying to get some meaning behind the numbers of suitors from Dulichium, Same, Zakynthos and Ithaca.

Dulichium/Dulichion is the most impressive, with 52 suitors. But is that number real or symbolic? Remember that the total number of people from Dulichium is greater than 52 when we consider adding the number of servants, which is six. So we have a total of 58. This number can only be the number of days in two short lunar months: $29 \times 2 = 58$ (Wood, 2011). As mentioned before, a lunar cycle is 29.5 days, but the ancients used whole numbers and alternated with 30-day and 29-day months. I see it as an inside joke for ancient calendar observers who understood *Odyssey* numbers. Unlike how it was treated in the catalogue of ships in *The Iliad* – a rather large region with forty ships, in

The Odyssey, Dulichium is given only 58 days – two short lunar months. Maybe in the original myth, some hostility existed between the real Ithaca and Dulichium?

Same (also spelled Sami) is represented by twenty-four men. This number represents the ancient two-year cycle (Διετηρις) which comprises 24 (lunar/synodic) months.

Zakynthos is represented by the number 20. This number is Meton's eikosieteris – the Metonic cycle of 19 years when the same moon phase repeats against the same constellations. People often refer to it as a nineteen-year cycle. Yes, it comprises a full nineteen years; however, the same moon phase appears again on the first day of the twentieth year.

Ithaca's number should be apparent by now. Ithaca has the most sacred number, twelve, representing the twelve months in the year. There were twelve suitors from Ithaca, twelve maidens that Odysseus punished, twelve axe heads that Odysseus shot an arrow through, and twelve ships that he commanded in *The Iliad.* Twelve is both Ithaca's and Odysseus' number. Every twelve months, the sun sets on Odysseus' tomb.

WHY DID HOMER CHOOSE ODYSSEUS?

So we have these Homeric "questions" lingering for over two thousand years, likely even longer. Why, of all founders/heroes of the Middle Helladic, did Homer choose Odysseus for his follow-up to *The Iliad*? I think there are several answers to this question.

I want to emphasize that even though the initial grandee buried in the royal tholos at the Lakithra peak should be identified as Odysseus, the pre-Homeric myths did not end with him. Instead, a "telescoping" of stories of others' life experiences, the history of the area with competing influential families, and the constellations and solar/lunar phenomena interacting with the tomb played a role in the making of the myth that reached Homer.

During the Bronze Age collapse on the mainland, the island of Kefalonia experienced "widespread development" and "general prosperity," judging by the mortuary landscape (Moschos, 2009). Communal cemeteries of chamber tombs were still in use until about 1050 BC. Trade continued, as mentioned before, and much amber had passed from

Kefalonia to the rest of Greece. Commercial transactions and myth retelling took place simultaneously. Hence, there was a "survivability of myths" element that Kefalonia, unlike other regions, may have had. The stability in Kefalonia also ensured little to no challenge of old myths and figures or how in autocratic regimes, past figures are "erased" from history after a revolution.

I believe the eventual fading of memories would have been between the Submycenaean period and well into the Iron age when the Krani acropolis took over the Archangelo center as the region's capital. By then, the mythology of Odysseus was already well known, though the accuracy of the geography suffered in retelling the myth.

Furthermore, we could characterize the civilization of Kokolata Livatho as a civilization of "timekeepers." From a cult center to cemeteries and tombs/graves, they marked and observed solar and lunar phenomena. They kept track of time as a religious exercise. This timekeeping was woven into their myths well before Homer's era. So if the epics were repositories of information, multi-disciplinary in nature, Homer must have thought it essential to convey that information, and the post-Bronze Age surviving myths of Odysseus served the purpose well. Homer combined a multiverse of heroes into a tight, incredible story involving two epics while retaining much older allegories and didactic elements.

These are my views based on reading and researching archaeoastronomy, comparative mythology, Minoan art interpretation, and the archaeological record of Kefalonia. These theories, I believe, will undoubtedly be tested, supported, and criticized by many in the future. I hope to see interdisciplinary cooperation, including astronomers, linguists, classicists, archaeogeneticists, and archaeologists. No one field could ever provide all the answers or give us a complete picture.

In the end, it looked like Homer, intentionally or not, was always telling us where we could find Odysseus' tomb. He must have known the astronomical allegories. Despite changing the story to fit a grander epic cycle, he knew the science/astronomy that existed parallel to the story should never be changed.

WHAT HAPPENED TO ITHACA?

I believe that the old Bronze Age center, Archangelo lost its power and influence, and a new center was created – at the nearby Krani hill, an existing settlement that outgrew the Archangelo settlement and, due to its elevation, offered better security. This conflict could have created new founder/foundation myths (that have not survived) and refugees of the old system who went to the island opposite what we now call Ithaca.

Furthermore, Odysseus' goal of being worshipped was parochial. It required both a specific religion and geography; that is to say, so long as people continued with this solar-based religion and worshipped at Kangelisses while viewing the peak at Lakithra, his story would always be retold on the festival of Apollo. However, I have doubts that it was the festival of Apollo. I believe that to be an Iron Age adaptation to the story.

The evolution of the Krani acropolis as the new main center, almost three kilometers away, ended thc old religious system and worship ritual. The new era pushed aside the old. Eventually, Kangelisses would be abandoned, and so would the local hero worship of the tomb at winter sunset. Memories of the actual religious practices began to fade. Only the stories remained. By 1050 BC, the cemeteries of Kokolata Livatho ceased being used.

As for the island we call Ithaca, apart from a long-considered cave named Polis, with few pottery sherds of the Bronze Age, there is not much else. Recent research has concluded that there was no cave at Polis. The "Polis cave" was most likely a meeting place used most often by the inhabitants of Kefalonia and Ithaca. A small, dependent island that interacted with the larger, wealthier island. (Souyoudzoglou 2022, p. 307 eBook)

The protogeometric pottery of Ithaca seems to have been influenced by the pottery of LHIIIC Kefalonia. (Souyoudzoglou 1999, p. 143) It is possible that some people from Kefalonia migrated to Ithaca during this period of change in southwestern Kefalonia and had enough standing to influence the pottery in Ithaca. They may not have only brought with them a pottery style but also particular hero worship as well - a hero worship that, for some reason, had been discontinued in Kefalonia post-Archangelo/ submycenaean era.

In the surrounding area of Archangelo, sherds of Early to Middle Helladic and Late Helladic ceramics have been found, but little to no protogeometric. Protogeometric sherds have been found at Krani, however. What we see in the Protogeometric pottery sherds is a migration and new concentration of settlement activity from the area of Kokolata-Livatho to Krani. Krani would later become one of the leading four centers on the island – the "Tetrapolis" Thucydides described.

Furthermore, as one Mycenaean center after another burned down on the mainland and existing political systems collapsed, there was a geopolitical vacuum in the Greek world. This collapse likely increased piracy during the Dark Age that followed. Krani, an elevated and easily defended hill, emerged as the new regional epicenter, which developed into a leading city with a powerful navy into the Hellenistic and Roman eras.

Archaeologist Klavs Randsborg (*Kephallenia,* 2002) proposed an interesting theory about the island called Ithaca today. He hypothesized that the Corinthians named it so in the 8th century BC for prestige because they had established a trading post on Ithaca.

Thus, I believe that Bronze Age Ithaca, or at least the society that created *The Odyssey* myth, was Archangelo, Kokolata, and the surrounding area in Kefalonia. It was inhabited by a large, organized population with a unique culture that expressed respect for the heavens in the solar design of their sacred sites. It was a society with a foundation myth incorporating a religious calendar that the rest of Greece found interesting and valuable enough to repeat and spread. These myths began to evolve in the retelling from countless bards up to the time of Homer.

WAS THERE EVER AN ITHACA?
THE BEST EXPLANATION

But maybe Ithaca was never even the name of a settlement or region. Perhaps it was an important descriptive term that later, after constant retellings of the original myth, erroneously became a place name due to its significance and the unawareness of the countless bards that retold the story without knowing the sun - royal tholos – horizon peak relationship. They focused on the character Odysseus returning home to a settlement and were oblivious to the actual sun returning to the tholos at that peak that marks the winter solstice. Both sun and Odysseus represent nostos – a return home.

On the blog *Homer's Ithaca* (Putnam-Cramer and Metaxas, 2018), an etymological analysis is done on that name. The meaning of "Ithaca" is interpreted as follows:

Ἰθεία **(ithia) + ακὴ (aki) =** Ἰθάκη (Ithaki/Ithaca) (the mountainous place with a sharp-pointed peak visible from afar and serving as a guide)

Ἰθύς **- ἰθεία - ἰθύ** = *guiding from afar or from opposite; straight; clearly visible; (of a mountain) steep*

Ἀκὴ **(ἀκὶς)** = point; sharp-pointed object; (of mountains) having high, sharp-pointed peaks.

The writer of the blog identifies this guiding peak with Mt. Ainos of Kefalonia, by far the largest mountain in the Ionian Sea and indeed a guide for seafarers navigating Western Greece, a major sea route that connects Greece with the northern lands along the Adriatic Sea and Italy.

Odysseus' "nostos," a yearning to return home, is for his homeland, Ithaca. The sun's "return" on the winter solstice, likely worshipped long before the actual Odysseus, was at that "guiding peak" of Lakithra. Let's suppose that the frequently mentioned number twelve in The Odyssey represents an entire solar cycle, a year. We now know that the locals measured the solar cycle using a peak on the horizon where the sun sets on the winter solstice every year. Is it a coincidence that the word "Ithaca" relates to a mountain peak as a guide? Let's look at the entire western horizon from the Kangelisses cemetery.

Fig. 53. Panorama photo, Kangelisses, western ridgeline as a solar calendar. Note: This is a wide-angle panorama image. Due to distortion, the peaks seem less prominent and farther away than if one were to see this view from Kangelisses.

I conclude that with its unique natural features, this horizon was a calendar to the ancients. The two unique peaks functioned as "markers" for the two solstice sunsets. Furthermore, the sun sets at each solstice just before the slope of each peak. I have not fully explored the summer solstice area, but from Google Earth, there seems to be a round structure covered by some vegetation. That round structure could be another tomb.

Thus, it is also highly likely that Ithaca was never an island, city, or settlement. For example, when Bronze Age visitors asked the locals of Kokolata-Livatho where the "West One," their famous leader, was buried, the locals pointed west at that renowned mountain peak. They said: "at that guiding peak/στην ιθάκη/ at ithaca." If we accept that much of *The Odyssey* is allegorical, then Odysseus returning to Ithaca would be the winter sun returning to that peak. Far from being an island or a city, it could be the name "Ithaca" was merely a description of a geographical feature that marked the winter solstice, distinctive moon phases, and the lunar standstill when viewed from the other sacred site – the solar cult center at Archangelo. When centuries of bards told the myth outside Kefalonia, that peak became an actual place name, and the royal tholos was forgotten.

It is interesting to note that when Homer refers to the places surrounding Ithaca, he mentions them in a specific order: Dulichion, Same, and wooded Zakynthos. If one were to go to the royal tholos and climb the peak above it to have an expansive view, they would see the following: the Paliki peninsula to the north, looking east, behind the mountains ahead, would be Same, which is a port city in Kefalonia, and looking south across the sea, lies the island of Zakynthos. Directly below is the Krania Valley, the village of Kokolata, and a sweeping view of all Livatho. To the west is the open sea beyond Greece. Basically, by looking from left to right and then down, the series would be Paliki, Same, Zakynthos, and then Kokolata and the surrounding valley floor.

IN CONCLUSION

This region's folklore was a collection of stories and celestial allegories inspired by the relationship of a tomb to the sky above. The folklore also included the adventures of their sailors in a new world and a civilization whose design was based on solar events, influenced by the non-Greek-speaking natives long before.

Their folklore and hero worship became a myth of calendrical allegories which represented the clockwork predictability of the deities they worshipped, a myth with a didactic story expressing the code of conduct of their society, and nostos, a yearning for a return to the homeland experienced by homesick sailors off on dangerous adventures.

It was celebrated by viewing a unique peak on the horizon where the winter solstice sun sets over the royal tomb, marking the day's rebirth. The location was also special because of the unique moon phases that predictably returned to the area of the royal tomb and the major lunar standstill, which occurred approximately every two decades, viewed from Archangelo. Centuries later, a talented bard wove this region's unique folklore into a masterpiece of an epic. Odysseus succeeded in being remembered.

My solar interpretation of the cult center at Archangelo Kokolata began my odyssey, ultimately leading me to what I believe is the royal tomb. This journey helped me better understand this civilization's deep roots in a small, overlooked corner of the world. Their folklore and ritual hero worship eventually grew into masterful stories that caught the attention of many ancients, including one gifted storyteller and, ultimately, the rest of the world.

I will admit I may have made some mistakes in my findings, or some theories may not be as strong in the eyes of others. But overall, these findings are extremely compelling and warrant further exploration. Furthermore, this is the first theory on Odyssean Ithaca that has yielded significant architectural results with a proven interpretation of their solar and celestial functions.

To understand the ancients, it is essential we do not view the solar phenomenon described in this book with modern knowledge. The ancients believed the sun was either a deity or controlled by a deity. Thus, to them, it was entirely plausible that the sun could arbitrarily cease its "stop" at "Ithaca", the guiding peak, and continue its voyage of diminishing days further along that horizon. This would have been a disaster for humanity. The location of the tomb of the solar hero at that guiding peak was what the ancients of the area relied on for the end of the diminishing day: the winter solstice. He was the solar hero that the sun briefly "met" and then reversed course by setting each day further away from the tomb. As a result, the day miraculously grew again. They collectively breathed a sigh of relief, worthy of celebration, and life continued.

Much work still lies ahead for many. Cooperation for a synergistic result is essential, and no individual field of study can claim this epic as their child because the Bronze and Iron Age ancients wove all fields of knowledge into their stories. Foremost, archaeology, but also archaeoastronomy, classics, linguistics, archaeogenetics, comparative literature, and Minoan and Mycenaean art history are all necessary tools. Then, we can better understand this unique period of history through the brilliant, complex stories the ancients left behind.

9

A MIDDLE HELLADIC LEADER AND
AN IRON AGE BARD

(Two short narratives that best illustrate what I believe happened.)

THE LEADER
Kangelisses, Kefalonia: circa 1600-1550 BC

Well into his sunset years, the aging West One stubbornly struggled to walk up to the flat hilltop of Kangelisses. He needed a moment to think about what he had to do to maintain this still fragile new society he had created and his legacy. Some leaders on the mainland had died young in glorious battle, and bards were now singing their stories. Unlike them, he had reached old age and feared becoming a fading memory.

Rosy fingered dawn warmed the air as he reached the top of the hill. He dismissed the two night-sky observers from their posts to be alone and then surveyed the land before him. He admired the large sheltered bay to the north, where Boötes, the plowman, impressively stands upright at night from late summer to early winter. That image had always imbued him with optimism about a future of sea exploration and visiting travelers from foreign capitals bearing exotic gifts.

Proudly he looked south to the well-known heavily forested majestic mountain - where both Orion and the equinox sun emerge - the tallest mountain west of the newly emerging Greek world blessed with a limitless supply of the best timber available. A well-known feature of the Ionian Sea, he was always honored that it was in his domain.

Then he turned west – where the sun deity sets to mark the beginning of the growing day, the celebration of regeneration, the unique day people had worshipped here since time began.

He had lived a life of challenges in ruling over this region. He cleverly convinced the locals to hold an archery competition so he could marry into a well-connected native family of the old local ways. Though he thought it unusual how they would worship by shaking trees and embracing boulders to see the deities, he was always careful not to upset the fragile balance between the old and the new emerging ways. Gradual assimilation was best, he always believed. People need time.

He lived during the catastrophe in the sea on the other side of the mainland, where the angry god Poseidon violently tossed an entire island, creating havoc in the Aegean and surrounding areas. Many religious conflicts ensued amongst the non-Greek-speaking natives. People were either fearful that they had upset the gods or maybe gave too much attention to the wrong ones and, as a result, questioned their long-held beliefs. Meanwhile, he and the leading families of his tribe, most of northern heritage, took advantage of the chaos that followed the catastrophe to elevate their standing and assimilate into the native elite socially.

He had visited the grand citadels rising on the mainland across the sea. He knew of the couple who reigned, along with the divine couple, the largest, most prosperous, and most advanced civilization in this area of the world. The magnificent labyrinthine Konoso [Knossos, Crete] compound was well known in his day, though its people recently suffered tremendously. His world was much more humble, safe, and still held promise. Many traveled through it as a gateway to the west, bringing news and stories from distant lands. Nonetheless, this land was also prone to earthquakes. Still, he somehow convinced the locals he could protect them from angry Poseidon, a god they had recently begun to fear, that apparently not even the sun could control.

Even though he had cleverly reorganized a community and secured the best farmland with plentiful water sources, a sense of insecurity still haunted him. Looking down, he thought about the wanaktes [leaders] on the mainland and how their people were prospering. Could he and his wife ever reach the fame of those in the grand citadels on the mainland?

He looked up again at that peak to the west where the divine sun always sets and always will. He observed the sky above and thought about how heroes of the deep past fill the night sky and live amongst the stars forever. Even those heroes above, permanently set in the sky, will outlast the wanaktes of the mainland, he thought to himself. But his jealousy lingered, so he continued thinking of a solution.

Constructing a great acropolis would be out of his reach, mainly because he had only a few years left. Moreover, the community was not big enough to construct time-consuming projects for the deities and his legacy. Most of the structures in the city were built with the sacred wood of the mountain. Yet he still envied the grand stone citadels and cemeteries rising on the mainland.

Then, a clever idea occurred to the man of many ways: he needed to be near the gods to be immortal. There was a way to become one with the sun deity on that sacred winter day. The location at that western peak - where he will become immortal and be reborn – at that unique sunset and on that holy day, he will be seen to return home every year and reunite with his wife as the divine couple did in the old legend.

It will be a grand tholos tomb at that peak, the regenerative tomb symbolic of the womb of the Great Mother with a path pointing to the winter solstice sunrise. Such burials were being used on the mainland after the wanaktes first learned of them on Kaptaru (Crete), the advanced civilization they all envied and emulated.

At night, the people will also see the constellations pass over his tomb and tell stories about him as they had done with the great past heroes, and worshippers will remember him forever.

He decided that the leading families should be buried here, on sacred Kangelisses. They could maintain legitimacy and influence but, at the same time, will always defer to his family because his tomb would be located well above their cemetery, at the sky's edge.

He resolved that the cemetery, while showing his tribes' northern roots in its construction, should also function as the ancient sun worship center in the city that marks the solstices and the equinoxes. This way, both tribes will be accommodated: the northern migrants and the sun following natives. These two tribes will also gradually become one, just as the Kangelisses cemetery used the form and function influenced by the two tribes to become one sacred space for all. It will be a sun deity worship center, fit for hero worship, not just a cemetery. With its brilliant views, Kangelisses will inspire stories, he satisfyingly thought.

Immortality through a glorious death in battle never happened to him. But he found a better way to be remembered. He will perpetually ride along with the sun's immortality. His kingdom will always be the westernmost settlement, where the sun sets in the emerging Greek world. Everyone will know of the "West One."

The wily West One of many ways had cleverly solved several vexing problems and unknowingly began what would culminate in a masterpiece of a story.

THE STORYTELLER

Ios, Greece: circa 700 BC

The well-traveled bard had already composed a famous epic, which drew heavily from an older story sung by countless bards before him. But unlike the older version, his story focused on one particular hero to explore the human psyche in depth. In the Greek world, all regions had legendary leaders of long-lost citadels, transformed into godlike heroes by local folklore and ritual hero cults. In the older versions of the story, these heroes of different centers joined forces to defeat a common enemy. It was a story that evolved amongst the various mainland centers, often told at weddings that forged alliances between citadels. It culturally bound the mainland and the ruling elites. Those heroes were the ones that were ultimately remembered – the ones of the deep past, the founders, not the anonymous last rulers that must have governed so irresponsibly that the Age of Heroes ended, leaving behind abandoned citadels with great walls built of colossal stones.

He had recently chosen one of those heroes from his first epic for his next story because this hero's origin tale was unique. The bard understood that the initial creators of this hero myth from the west had woven a story that contained the predictable movements of the sun and moon, which served as units of time, and the constellations, which served as navigational guides. It was a very ancient calendar, an extremely useful tool for any serious civilization engaged in farming and sea voyages. The hero's travels and the contrast between the unknown wild west and the civilized east intrigued him.

This story, however, would be very different in tone, scope, and setting. He had experienced a lot in life and reached a ripe age to create such an engaging story of a man's love for his family and homeland. Besides, this time he would also focus on developing essential and influential female characters from the deep, forgotten past when the religion was more feminine-centric and solar-related. These goddesses or goddess-like mortals would assist or hinder this hero in his solar quest. He needed a challenge: a very different story and yet a continuation of his first masterpiece.

He often wondered if this myth's allegories of the sun and moon were also based on events such as a solar hero worship at a long-lost cult center or tomb. Much had changed in the central Ionian Sea, where this folklore had been created and initially told. Four independent citadels had risen in the land of the Kephallenes. The smaller, much less populated island across the channel was now called Ithaca by the Corinthians ever since they opened a trading post that served the western sea trade route. [Well after Homer's time, the Corinthians would change this hero's lineage claiming their first King Sysiphus was the birth father of Odysseus.]

He thought again of the solar theme of that original myth. Why such a repetitive solar focus? It can't be just about a calendar, he thought. In real life, this ancient hero must have somehow cleverly devised a way to link himself permanently with the immortal sun. Nonetheless, with those allegories, he could be creative with wordplay, an essential element of epics for those that understood. Respect and enjoyment of the epics from the masses were important, but to also earn the respect of wise elders, other bards, and especially a competition judge that understood the layers of a story and wordplays was what he relished most.

* * *

It was his first night singing this new tale. He rose from his seat and walked into the middle of the eager audience, the fire nearby giving him a unique glow that emphasized him as the center of attention. He raised his arms in the air, as he always did, with eyes closed, chin raised. His now aging body was trembling for effect to show he was in the process of being fully possessed by the muse that would tell the story through him. Suddenly, his eyes flashed wide open, and his voice boomed out the first five words:

"Ανδρα μοι ἔννεπε, Μοῦσα, πολύτροπον!"
"Of a man, speak to me, Muse, he of many ways!"

BIBLIOGRAPHY

Anthony, D. W. 2007. *The Horse, the Wheel, and Language: How Bronze-Age Riders from the Eurasian Steppes Shaped the Modern World*. Princeton, NJ: Princeton University Press.

Blomberg, M. and Henriksson, G. 2014. Minoan Astronomy, in C.L.N. Ruggles (ed.), *Handbook of Archaeoastronomy and Ethnoastronomy* (New York: Springer 2015) 1432-1435. DOI 10.1007/978-1-4614-6141-8_141.

Bittlestone, R. Diggle, J. Underhill, J. 2005. *Odysseus Unbound: The Search for Homer's Ithaca*. Cambridge: Cambridge University Press.

Brack-Bernsen, L. 2007. The 360-Day Year in Mesopotamia, in Steele, J. M. (ed.), *Calendars and Years: Astronomy and Time in the Ancient Near East*. Oxford: Oxbow Books, 155-186 (eBook)

Cline, E.H. 2014. *1177 B.C.: The Year Civilization Collapsed*. S.L.: Princeton University Pres.

Curry, A. 2019. World of the Griffin Warrior. *Archaeology Magazine*. [online] Sept/Oct. 2019. Available from: https://www.archaeology.org/ issues/352-1909/features/7900-greece-pylos-mycenaean-warrior-grave

d'Huy, J. 2016 Scientists Trace Society's Myths to Primordial Origin, *Scientific American*, Sept. 2016. [online] Available from: https://www.scientificamerican.com /article/ scientists-trace-society-rsquo-s-myths-to-primordial-origins/

Edmunds, L. 2014. *Approaches to Greek Myth*. 2nd ed. Baltimore: Johns Hopkins University Press.

Evans, A. 1901. *The Mycenaean Tree and Pillar Cult and its Mediterranean Relations, with Illustrations from Recent Cretan Finds*. London: Macmillan.

Frame, D. 1978. *The Myth of Return in Early Greek Epic*. New Haven: Yale University Press. Available from: https://chs.harvard.edu/book/frame-douglas-the-myth-of-return-in-early-greek-epic/

Gimbutas, M., and Dexter, M.R. 1999. *The Living Goddesses*. Berkeley: University of California Press.

Google LLC., 2021. *Google Earth Pro*. Versions 6 and 7

Grey, S. 2018. Homer's Odyssey in the Hands of its Allegorists: Many Paths to Explain the Cosmos, in Chiara Ferella and Cilliers Breytenbach (eds.), *Paths of Knowledge. Interconnection(s) between Knowledge and Journey in the Greco-Roman World*, Berlin: Edition Topoi, 189–215

Guglielmino, S.L., Cipolla, P.B., Rizzo Giudice, I. 2017. Astronomy in the Odyssey: The *Status Quaestionis*. in Orlando, A. (eds), *The Light, The Stones and The Sacred. Astrophysics and Space Science Proceedings*, vol 48. Springer, Cham.

Günkel-Maschek, U. 2016. Establishing the Minoan "Enthroned Goddess" in the Neopalatial Period: Images, Architecture, and Elitist Ambition. in Alram-Stern, E., Blakolmer, F., Deger Jalkotzy, S., Laffineur, R., and Weilhartner, J. (eds.), *Metaphysis: Ritual, Myth and Symbolism in the Aegean Bronze Age. Aegaeum 39*. Leuven – Liège: Peeters: 255–62.

Henriksson, G. and Blomberg, M. 1997. Evidence for Minoan Astronomical Observations from the peak sanctuaries on Petsophas and Traostalos. in *Opuscula Atheniensia. Annual of the Swedish Institute at Athens (OpAth)* 21, Stockholm 1997. ISSN: 0078-5520. 99-114. Available from: https://minoanastronomy.mikrob.com/ pdf/1996 _Petsophas.pdf

Heraclitus, 1st cent. 2005 Trans. by Russell, D. A., Konstan, D. *Heraclitus: Homeric problems / edited and translated by Donald A. Russell and David Konstan*. Atlanta: Society of Biblical Literature

Homer. *The Odyssey*. 1919 Trans. by A.T. Murray, Cambridge MA: Harvard University Press.Availablefrom:https://www.perseus.tufts.edu/hopper/text?doc=Perseus:text:1999.01.0136

Kavvadias, P., 1914. Προϊστορική Αρχαιολογία εν Ελλάδα, Athens.

Kyriakidis, E. 2005. Unidentified Floating Objects on Minoan Seals. *American Journal of Archaeology* 109:137-154.

Lazaridis, I., Alpaslan-Roodenberg, S., et al., 2022. A Genetic Probe into the Ancient and Medieval History of Southern Europe and West Asia, *Science* 377, pp. 940–951, 26 August 2022

Lazaridis, I., Mittnik, A., Patterson, N., Mallick, S., Rohland, N., Pfrengle, S., Furtwängler, A., Peltzer, A., Posth, C., Vasilakis, A., McGeorge, P.J.P., Konsolaki-Yannopoulou, E., Korres, G., Martlew, H., Michalodimitrakis, M., Özsait, M., Özsait, N., Papathanasiou, A., Richards, M. and Roodenberg, S.A. 2017. Genetic origins of the Minoans and Mycenaeans. *Nature*, [online] 548(7666), pp.214–218. doi:10.1038/nature23310. Available from: https://www.nature.com/articles/nature23310

Leeming, David. 2003. *From Olympus to Camelot: The World of European Mythology*. New York, NY: Oxford University Press.

Levaniouk, Olga. 2011. *Eve of the Festival: Making Myth in Odyssey 19*. Hellenic Studies Series 46. Washington, DC: Center for Hellenic Studies

Lewartowski, K. 2019. Combat, Myths and Seals in the Griffin Warrior Times, *Studies in Ancient Art and Civilisation*. 23. December 2019. 73-93.

Marinatos, N. 2010. *Minoan Kingship and the Solar Goddess: A Near Eastern Koine*, Chicago: University of Illinois Press.

Marinatos, N. 1993. *Minoan Religion: Ritual, Image, and Symbol*, Columbia: University of South Carolina Press.

Marks, J. 2008. *Zeus in The Odyssey*. Hellenic Studies Series 31. Washington, DC: Center for Hellenic Studies [online] Available from: http://nrs.harvard.edu/urn-3:hul.ebook:CHS_Marks.Zeus _in_the_ Odyssey.2008.

Merkouri C. and Kouli M. 2012. The Spatial Distribution and Location of Bronze Age Tumuli in Greece in *Ancestral Landscape. Burial mounds in the Copper and Bronze Ages* (Central and Eastern Europe – Balkans – Adriatic – Aegean, 4th-2nd millennium B.C.) Proceedings of the International Conference held in Udine, May 15th-18th 2008. Lyon : Maison de l'Orient et de la Méditerranée Jean Pouilloux, pp. 203-217. (Travaux de la Maison de l'Orient et de la Méditerranée. Série recherches archéologiques, 58)

Metaxas, O. 2022. Diverging Trajectories Within the West Mycenaean Koine: the Evidence from Kefalonia, In Souyoudzoglou-Haywood, C. and Papoulia, C. (eds.), *Archaeology of the Ionian Sea: Landscapes, Seascapes and the Circulation of People, Goods and Ideas from the Palaeolithic to the end of the Bronze Age.* Oxford: Oxbow Books, 169-178.

Moschos, I. 2009. Evidence of Social Re-organization and Reconstruction in Late Helladic IIIC Achaea and Modes of Contacts and Exchange via the Ionian and Adriatic Sea, in E. Borgna and P. Cassola Guida (eds.), *Dall-Egeo ad Adriatico: organizzazioni sociali, modi di scambio e interazione in età post-palaziale (XII-XI sec. a.C.* pp. 345-414.

Murray, G. 1924. *The Rise of the Greek Epic: Being A Course of Lectures Delivered at Harvard University*, Clarendon Press, Oxford 211-212 [online] Available from: https://archive.org/details/riseofgreekepicb00murruoft/ page/210/mode/2up?ref=ol&view=theater

Nagy, G. 1973. *Phaethon, Sappho's Phaon, and the White Rock of Leukas.* Harvard Studies in Classical Philology, Vol. 77 (1973) Available from: https://chs.harvard.edu/chapter/chapter-9-phaethon-sapphos-phaon-and-the-white-rock-of-leukas-reading-the-symbols-of-greek-lyric-pp-223-262/

Nicolson, A. 2014. *The Mighty Dead: Why Homer Matters*, London: William Collins

Oikonomidis S., Papayiannis A., and Tsonos A. 2011. The Emergence and the Architectural Development of the Tumulus Burial Custom in NW Greece (Epirus and the Ionian Islands) and Albania and its Connections to Settlement Organization, *Borgna and Moller Celka* (eds.), pp. 185-201

Papadopoulos, J., 2022. *The Excavation at Agios Athanasios / School of Homer: The Archaeological Evidence for the Palace of Odysseus on Ithaca,* (self-pub.)

Papathanassiou, M. K., 2008. Homeric Calendar and Helios Charioteer, S.A. Paipetis (ed.), *Science and Technology in Homeric Epics*, pp. 357–368. © Springer Science Business Media BV 2008

Philippa-Touchais, A., 2004 Livatho. in *Bulletin de correspondance hellénique*. Volume 128-129, livraison 2.2, 2004. pp. 1374-1375.

Putnam-Cramer, H. and Metaxas, O. 2018. Searching for the exact location of "clearly-seen" Ithaca, the capital of Odysseus' Mycenaean island Kingdom in Western Greece. *Homer's Ithaca,* September 2018. Available at: http://homericithaca.blogspot.com/2018/09/serching-for-exact-location-of-clearly.html

Roodenberg, S.A. 2017. Genetic origins of the Minoans and Mycenaeans. *Nature*, [online] 548(7666), pp.214–218. doi:10.1038/nature23310. Available from: https://www.nature.com/articles/nature23310

Rethemiotakis, G. 2016. The ›Divine Couple‹ ring from Poros and the Origins of the Minoan Calendar, *Mitteilungen des Deutschen Archaologischen Instituts - Athenische Abteilung* 131-132 (2016/2017): 1-29.

Sakellariou, M. 2009. ΕΛΛΗΝΙΚΑ ΕΘΝΗ ΚΑΤΑ ΤΗΝ ΕΠΟΧΗ ΤΟΥ ΧΑΛΚΟΥ, *Research Center for Antiquity of the Academy of Athens.*

Scott, J. A. 1917. Odysseus as a Sun-God, *Classical Philology* Vol. 12, No. 3 Jul. 1917, The University of Chicago Press pp. 244-252.

Souyoudzoglou-Haywood, C. 2018. Archaeology and the Search for Homeric Ithaca, *Acta Archaeologica* 89.1 145-158.

Souyoudzoglou-Haywood, C. 2008. Interpreting the Bronze Age Landscape of Kefalonia, A Preliminary review from the Livatho Valley Survey, *Dioskouroi: Studies Presented to WG*

Cavanagh and CB Mee on the Anniversary of Their 30-year Joint Contribution to Aegean Archaeology, pp. 237-251. British Archaeological Reports Limited 2008

Souyoudzoglou-Haywood, C. 1999. *The Ionian Islands in the Bronze and Early Iron Age 3000-800 BC*, Liverpool: Liverpool University Press.

Souyoudzoglou-Haywood, C. 2022. Islands in the Stream: a Maritime Perspective of the South-Central Ionian Islands in the Late Bronze Age, in Souyoudzoglou-Haywood, C. and Papoulia, C. (eds.), *Archaeology of the Ionian Sea: Landscapes, Seascapes and the Circulation of People, Goods and Ideas from the Palaeolithic to the end of the Bronze Age.* Oxford: Oxbow Books, 117-136

Theodossiou, E., Manimanis, V. N., Mantarakis, P., and Dimitrijevic, M. S., 2011. Astronomy and Constellations in Homeric Iliad and Odyssey, in Journal of Astronomical History and Heritage (ISSN 1440-2807), Vol. 14, No. 1, 22 – 30

Vasilakis, A. 2020. Υστεροελλαδικό ελλειψοειδές μέγαρο στα Τζαννάτα Πόρου, Νέα στοιχεία για την Υστεροελλαδική περίοδο στην Κεφαλονιά. In D.F. Markatou (ed.), *ΙΑ΄ Διεθνές Πανονιο Συνέδριο, Επτανησιακός Βίος και Πολιτισμός, Κεφαλονιά,* 21-25 Μαΐου 2018, *Πρακτικά. Τόμος: V Αρχαιολογία,* 53-74. Argostoli: Εταιρεία Κεφαλληνιακων Ιστορικων Ερευνών.

Volker, H. 2012. Yamnaya Groups and Tumuli west of the Black Sea. in *Ancestral Landscape. Burial mounds in the Copper and Bronze Ages (Central and Eastern Europe – Balkans – Adriatic – Aegean, 4th-2nd millennium B.C.)* Proceedings of the International Conference held in Udine, May 15th-18th 2008. Lyon : Maison de l'Orient et de la Méditerranée Jean Pouilloux, 2012. 535-555. (Travaux de la Maison de l'Orient et de la Méditerranée. Série recherches archéologiques, 58)

Wood, F. and K. 2011. *Homer's Secret Odyssey*, Gloucestershire: The History Press.

Zotti, G., Hoffmann, S., Wolf, A., Chéreau, F. and Chéreau G. 2021. The Simulated Sky: Stellarium for Cultural Astronomy Research, *Journal of Skyscape Archaeology.* 6. 221-258. 10.1558/jsa.17822.

Index

CPSIA information can be obtained
at www.ICGtesting.com
Printed in the USA
BVHW012309230123
656912BV00005B/46